MW00616394

EX LIBRIS

HOSPITALITY FOR
HEALING

Recovering Care Traditions for Convalescence

MELISSA NAASKO

PARK END BOOKS

Sugar Land
2022

Hospitality For Healing:
Recovering Care Traditions for Convalescence
Copyright ©2022 Melissa Naasko

Cover design: Summer Kinard

Publisher's Cataloging-in-Publication Data

Names: Naasko, Melissa, 1976-, Author
Title: Hospitality for Healing: recovering care traditions for convalescence
Description: Sugar Land [Texas]: Park End Books, 2022.

Identifiers: ISBN: 978-1-953427-12-0
Subjects: RELIGION/Christianity/Orthodox
COOKING/Health & Healing/General

www.parkendbooks.com

TABLE OF CONTENTS

DEDICATIONS

BOOKS ARE FUNNY THINGS. When you pick them up, you see the author's name on the cover. The title page also has the publisher's name, but that is the name of the company and not of every single person who turned a random idea into a concrete plan and then into an actual book that you can hold in your hands. This book, like all books, was a team effort. I must thank Summer Kinard, my dear friend, who also happens to own Park End Books. Thanking her means also thanking her family who generously share her and her many talents with the world. I owe a debt of gratitude to her husband, Andrew, and her children Michael, Ana, John, Basil, and Rosie.

Because she is nowhere on the cover or title page, I must not forget to thank Korrine York (RN, BSN, and Certified Pediatric Nurse) who is my medical consultant. She provided an enormous amount of guidance in my research and offered her clinical experience to help guide my recipe research. She also helped me to craft a solid foundation for a healing diet for all kinds of conditions. Despite her careful attention and steady diligence, I am still me, and as the author of the book, all errors are my own fault. I am simply grateful for her support which prevents more errors. Thank you also to her family who shared her with me when they had so much else going in their lives, to her husband JY, and her beautiful children, GY and EY. Her husband is currently in seminary, and I have such great hope for their future parishioners. They will be in excellent hands.

My name would not be anywhere on this book if not for the love and support of my patient family including my husband, eleven children, and one daughter-in-love. They put up with my recipe testing and research and give me the time to slink away and write, only for me to later force them to read edits upon edits while I tried to create the right tone. Father Benjamin, Joseph, Noelle, Raymond, Maria, Elijah, Gregory, Jack, Isabel, Veronica, Cristina, Sophia, and Claudia: you are so generous, and moreover kind, with your evaluations of my efforts. You make this possible.

I absolutely have to thank my mother, Karen, for the gallons and gallons of her life-sustaining chicken and dumplings that she made for me during the time when I was convalescent. You would think that after weeks and weeks of eating this at least once a day that maybe I might not have any taste for it. Yet, I still crave it and probably always will. It tastes like a mother's love.

I wish that I could personally thank Ann Sullivan. She passed away thirteen years ago, but she is always in my heart. It is my hope that I may grow in grace and the love of God and to every

2

day be more and more like her. You don't know her now, but I can promise that you will love her. You will get to meet her in the conclusion of this book.

I also owe a debt of gratitude to my spiritual father, Father Michael Carney, who makes sure I at least try to be in the proper place to be receptive to hospitality. Thank you to his incomparable wife, Matushka Darya. She is a model of hospitality to her parishioners and iconography students as well as a paragon of generosity as she shares her husband with his many spiritual children.

Lastly, thank you to each and every person who has ever read what I write. When I sit down to write, I think of you and your kind emails and messages and warm hugs at conferences and I am so grateful that I get to interact with each and every one of you. Even if we never meet, I pray for the people who listen to me talk and read what I write. I humbly ask that you pray for me as well.

INTRODUCTION: WHAT IS HOSPITALITY?

*"When he said to his disciples, "The harvest is plentiful,
but the laborers are few;"*
Matthew 9:37

MY LIFE REVOLVES AROUND FOOD. One of the greatest privileges of my life is my vocation as a priest's wife, and other than being a wife, mother, and daughter, it is the primary way in which I live out hospitality. My husband is a Russian Orthodox priest attached to a monastery. Being at a monastery gives me so many opportunities to practice hospitality in the congenial and welcoming sense as well as hospitality in the nursing sense. The weekly cycle begins with Tuesday night and the coffee and tea with the catechumens and young adults. Wednesday night is Vespers and supper with a Bible study to follow. Then Sunday comes with the need for prosphora, the holy bread for communion, and the main dish for the parish lunch, which I cook and serve for the entire community with my children's help. I have learned to keep a ready supply of cooked and frozen koliva, the traditional dish for funerals and annual services for the dead, so that when some brokenhearted person comes to ask my husband for a pannikhida, I can have one ready with thirty minutes notice.

Great Lent brings the weekly pannikhidas and two Presanctified Liturgies, for which I cook Lenten soup for all who attend. For Pascha, I will make the artos which will be broken and distributed on Bright Saturday. I boil red eggs for the Pascha liturgy and the festive kulichi breads that we serve at Pascha breakfast and give to each family. For Radonitsa, I will dye even more eggs so that they can be taken out and placed on the graves of those whom we love and whom we hope to see in Paradise one day.

I cook for memorials and baptisms and for high feasts. I cook for visits from pilgrims, visitors to the monastic community, and for the bishop. The children always look forward to the bishop's visit because I make homemade donuts. I stand in the kitchen to fry them while people line up at the window with empty plates and open mouths.

I cook for monastics when they have name days and tonsures and when they are sick. Monks do not have wives living with them to make sure that they eat and drink enough fluids while recovering. I bring dinners, I remind them to drink, and I encourage them to rest as much as anyone can ever expect a monk to actually rest. It is at these moments that even the most ascetic and stoic monks soften, and I see another side of them, one that asks for seconds or thirds of soup, and our bond grows a little through the reciprocity of hospitality. Monks no longer celebrate birthdays after they are tonsured, but I have baked cake for the community to celebrate our joy at having them with us. We invite the monastics to sit with us while we celebrate.

I cook for parishioners when they are sick, and I bring food to their homes. I have made batch after batch of homemade broth and taken it to the hospital room of a parishioner with cancer. I feed the community with a food bank. While sometimes people come to the church, I have brought boxes of food to homes when COVID prevents them from going out to shop. I mother my husband's spiritual children with the same love I have for my own children. This relationship runs two ways. I need to do this, I was made to do this, and God has tasked me with this. Still, every opportunity gives me a chance to deny my own will and consider the needs of others, and every loaf of bread, every pot of soup, and every donut makes me a better person, one who is less selfish and more focused on God.

People have an inherent need for hospitality; we both deeply want to offer it and crave it in our times of need. It is the relationship that binds us in our human frailty and ties us together, creating bonds that will extend past the time we are together. I have offered and I have received hospitality, and it makes me incredibly grateful for both times. I want to help others enter into this beautiful circle of hospitality, one of both giving and receiving. This book arrives out of this sense of gratitude and a deep knowledge that this is desperately needed right now.

Hospitality is rooted in the concept of compassion, particularly to visitors. The words hospitality, hospitable, hospital, and hospice all come from the same Latin root, *hospes* or guest, visitor. Hospitality is the compassion we extend to that visitor. The people who come into our lives, the ones whom we care for, are either long or short-term companions in our lives, and hospitality is the relationship that we have with each other. Our lives will intersect with many others, and we can offer hospitality to them for the period of time that they are with us. No matter what the circumstances, hospitality always has a common thread, and even though it may look very different, it will also look very similar.

One of my favorite memories will always be of a particularly stoic monk who had surgery. One of the challenges of living in such a far-flung region is that obtaining medical treatment often means driving a few hundred miles, round trip. This monk had to be driven just over 100 miles to get back home and would need a soft meal before retreating to his bed for rest, and I planned on making soup for him. Russian monks usually forsake meat, and he was no exception; additionally, it was a fasting period, so he needed a soup with no dairy. My experience as a recipe developer serves me well in these moments, and I put my hands to work doing the work that they know best.

I roasted carrots, onions, garlic, and a little ginger with olive oil until it was all golden, syrupy, and intensely fragrant. I blended it with coconut milk until it was smooth and creamy, and I brought it to the monastery. I knew it was nourishing and mechanically soft so it was what he needed, but it also turned out to be exactly what he wanted.

I watched his stoicism melt, and he was very briefly childlike as he asked for another bowl, and even another after that. He is a very strong man and exceedingly capable, and in many other situations I have asked for his help. But then it was his turn to receive hospitality. Some people are hard to know; people like this monk hold much back, but not at this moment. At this moment, he let me know how much he appreciated the soup before he was helped up to bed by his brother monk. He even texted me from bed to thank me. I will always have this moment, this moment in which I shared with this monk and he shared back with me, and we were very briefly connected through the act of hospitality.

Hospitality is a broad and reaching term, perhaps broader than we initially think. When we think about what hospitality is, we may first think about what it means to be hospitable. We might think about what it is that someone does that makes them a hospitable person. It might have something to do with being warm and friendly and generous in giving whatever is necessary to make others comfortable. We might think about those specifics, what exactly one does. We might think of fluffy towels and clean sheets, sweet-smelling soaps in the bathroom, and pleasant drinks at the right temperature and at the right moment. There is so much love and generosity in these actions. This is the extent of the hospitality that most of us understand, and while it is good, it is not always enough. Sometimes we need another, deeper level of hospitality.

Sometimes, we need the hospital. This is the place where people who are sick or injured are taken so that they can be carefully cared for and treated with an intensive and perhaps aggressive type of hospitality, things like surgeries and medications. There are some parallels here to the good host or hostess; the same comforts of clean sheets and specially prepared meals, though of a different sort, are a part of the hospitality of the hospital. Hospitals also entail a deeper kind of hospitality, one where the body is cared for in an even more intimate way. There are wounds and illnesses that require surgery and medication, which are brought to the patient in the same way, also at the precise moment when they are most helpful. The body must be washed and kept clean when the patient is not capable of doing this for himself, and this requires the physical touch of others. There is a particular magnanimity in the nursing effort found in hospitals that makes this kind of hospitality distinct. It is the hospitality that is devoted to healing, to providing the resources for one to convalesce and recover.

As we think of the particular hospitality that we find in the hospital, it is not a far leap to also think of hospices and the particular brand that is found there. We know this as the place and the sort of care that is completely devoted to providing physical and psychological comforts to the dying. While hospice is not necessarily directed toward physical healing, our hospitality toward the dying does, by extension, offer a kind of healing, though it is not of the body. Along with the care devoted to them, we offer this to their families as well. This kind of hospitality holds the same warmth and compassion we see in the hospital devoted to another end, not towards simple comforts or to healing, but to coming to terms with death. We still have the fresh bedding, sometimes meals, bathing, and still more medication and medical procedures, but these all happen in an atmosphere that is filled with the consciousness of this short-lived opportunity to serve another person. The resolution is different here. When there is no healing to be had, only the comforts, it increases our desire to pour out more compassion and more devotion and more and more of everything, because our opportunities to be so giving are very limited. As human persons, our desire to serve and to give is a strong drive.

One of the most consistent ways in which we do this is by feeding others; it is a common thread in all forms of hospitality.

Food is an integral part of life. We know that we need food to live, and this changes the relationship we have with food and eating. Feeding others is deeply life-giving, and in caring for others this way we let them know how much we value them. Preparing food for others allows us to acknowledge this human need for nourishment, and in doing so we nourish more than the body. We nourish the soul. When we feed others, we feed them with love. Others can know this love, and it can serve to strengthen them in times of illness and injury when their own resources are in short supply. It is a powerful thing to know that we are being loved and cared for and fed, and it is a strong motivator for caregivers to know that our efforts are felt and known. When we don't know what else to do, when we don't know how to love someone in the way that they need, we can fill that space with food.

Most people in my generation and even of my parents' generation have not been educated on how to feed people while they heal from illness or injury. If you are like me, you might have sat in the chair next to the hospital bed and listened carefully as the doctors recommended a soft diet or a pureed diet, and perhaps you even received a list of foods. You might have looked at that list and not really understood much at all. I have to admit that in the past I did not really know why a doctor would prescribe a certain kind of diet or really what the limitations of the diet were. I might have or might have not always followed the lists carefully, because they just felt so random. My understanding was limited to an awareness of a physical ability to eat. I never would have served steak to someone recovering from a root canal. That said, I only knew to serve ice cream for someone needed soft foods. I would not have known what else to give them. Heaven, help them if they needed more support than this, because I certainly couldn't feed them!

My grandmothers always instinctively knew how to feed people. Immediately, they would line up the pots in the kitchen and get to work. We younger people often rely on a very limited set of skills and recipes. I think a lot of this is because we expect that only the kitchens of hospitals really need to have any knowledge of dietary needs. My grandmothers birthed babies and cared for sick family members in makeshift infirmaries tucked into small bedrooms in small homes. They called on the wisdom that was developed over the years of personally caring for others when hospitals were expensive and reserved for those with the means to pay. I thought they were a little silly, that it was like playing nurse, but I was wrong. They had a skill set that I didn't have, that my mother and father didn't have, and it means that they were better prepared for what their families might have endured. It was forgotten wisdom that I wished my family had when it was my turn to need it.

I was a recipe developer and caterer when my tenth baby was born back in 2010. In September of that year, I was delivered of a perfectly beautiful baby girl whom we named Sophia. We had expected a complicated delivery, but it had gone badly, very badly. I crashed on the postpartum floor, and I had to be rushed into a five-hour surgery to stem massive internal bleeding. The situation was complicated by the fact that my surgeons had both left, and the deck doc was actively delivering a baby.

While they waited for help, the anesthesiologist had to step in to manage the situation while they waited for a surgeon. After an infusion of albumin, I was conscious enough to overhear a conversation between this confident, capable anesthesiologist and a very frightened nurse. The nurse had bags of blood in her hand and was near tears.

"I don't know how to do non-crossmatch blood. This is OB. We don't do this here."

I could hear the doctor from somewhere behind my head, "I will do it."

Growing up with doctors and nurses in my family, I knew that if they were using non-crossmatched blood, it meant that they did not have time to do a test and in desperation would rely on universal blood. I might be dying, actually dying. They didn't have minutes to spare. It was the last thing I can remember until waking up on a ventilator in the intensive care unit a day later. Later, my obstetrician said that when I was open, he realized that they were in over their heads, so he called in the level one trauma surgeons from the emergency room, the ones who handle traumatic gunshot wounds and other urban crises.

After being weaned to breathing on my own, I found myself unable to sit up fully. My belly was covered with a total of twenty inches of incisions in an inverted T shape, all held together with staples. My jaws ached and my teeth were no longer lining up because the muscles were strained. I had resisted the device placed in my mouth to hold my mouth open when I was intubated. The size of my incisions caused so much pain and a lack of muscle strength that I was unable to sit up to eat, and on top of that challenge, I had no strength in my jaws to chew. My throat ached horribly, and just the thought of swallowing was painful. For once in my life, I had no desire to eat at all, even though I needed it. I was recovering from two different surgeries plus childbirth and was trying to incorporate seventeen units of transfused blood. I had bled out more, much more, than my total blood volume, and it had been replaced in a complicated procedure by which they tried to supply new blood at the same rate at which I lost it. I needed rest, but I also needed to eat in order to have the strength to recover. I knew this, but I could hardly bring myself to do it.

I knew how to cook. I knew how to develop recipes. I knew how to accommodate various palates. Still, I lacked the strength to even think about what I needed and certainly did not have the ability to communicate it. My father was a director of nursing at another facility. He knew what my needs were but did not know how to make these practical. He just relied on those basic lists of unpalatable but safe and only marginally nutritious foods. My husband was trying to care for a newborn and nine older children with the teens pitching in as much as possible, and he didn't have the headspace to think about food. Feeding me fell to my mother, who found the fallback position of my childhood favorite. It was soft. It was nourishing. It was warm. It was high in protein. It was her very traditional and completely from scratch chicken and dumplings soup, and she made it by the gallon.

I am not a picky eater by nature; I am actually very adventurous. I love to cook, and I love to eat; I had never before struggled to find the will to eat. Just staying awake and trying to remember who had come to visit consumed all my available energy. I even missed my oldest son's birthday and did not realize it for a week, but I still wanted my mother's soup. It was warm and soothed my sore jaw muscles. It was soft and easy for me to eat and didn't require chewing. It was filled with fresh vegetables that were cooked slowly in homemade chicken broth to fully soften them. My mother carefully peeled and minced every piece to be incredibly tiny, and she cooked them longer than normal. The soup nearly melted in my mouth. It was rich and soothing and turned out to be the perfect balance of meeting my nutritional needs and physical limitations. I ate this for nearly every meal for weeks–maybe as many as six weeks! I don't actually remember, but the important thing is that I am here to tell you about it.

Fast forward to the early weeks of the Covid-19 global pandemic when my dear friend (and publisher!), Summer, and her husband and children were all infected with the coronavirus. When her sister became ill, despite the fact that Summer was not even quite on her feet yet, she asked Summer to come to stay with her. Summer dove into hospitality in the traditional Christian sense and built a little hospital in her home. When the fog began to clear, she began collecting convalescent cookbooks from the early 20th Century to help her rediscover the common wisdom about recuperation that we used to have. Being a Covid long-hauler, she had months of practice in caring for her own body and of those of her husband and children and sister. She devoured these books and fed her family with the knowledge she garnered from them. She worked to feed herself as well as these loved ones properly to promote their healing, and she came out the other side with a strength and resilience that I find so admirable. This experience gave her the idea for this book, and she reached out to me. To say I was excited to take on this project is an understatement.

I think we, as modern people, need this book. We have a need for hospitality, both to offer and receive it, but we often don't know how to satisfy this desire. There is no guide like this on the shelves right now, and we need it. We have collectively forgotten how to feed those who need strength to recover from illness. We must know how to feed those who are ill, because they cannot feed themselves. It is up to us. Living through a global pandemic teaches us a lot of things. On that long list is how to care for family members at home, a critical skill, and for many of us, it is lacking. I deeply feel the need to resolve this. We should be able to care for others. I see it as an extension of my Christian Faith and my vocation as a priest's wife. When I feed people who are sick or suffering, I am feeding Christ's lambs. When I serve the least of these, I serve Him. It is an act of gratitude and hope and love, and it is as good for me as it is for those I cook for.

I am very grateful for the opportunity to write this book. I am grateful for the experience I had which gives me the awareness of the problem that I want to address. I am grateful to God for my life and for those ten children who did not lose their mother that day. I am also supremely grateful for the eleventh surprise baby who was born after my recuperation. I am grateful for my husband who was always by my side and clearly meant his vows, because he had to help me to the bathroom and even bathed me during my long recovery. We could not have survived if not for the friends and our extended community who did our housework and laundry and brought meals and diversions for the children. I am also deeply and profoundly grateful for my mother and her love that tasted like slow-roasted chicken and garlic. I can never express the depth of my gratitude for so many things, so I will turn it into a book. I hope and pray it helps many people who are either convalescing or caring for someone who is. May this work be blessed, and may I be equal to the calling.

CHAPTER ONE:
CONVALESCENT DIETS

"For I was hungry and you gave Me food; I was thirsty and you gave Me drink; I was a stranger and you took Me in; I was naked and you clothed Me; I was sick and you looked after me..."
Matthew 25:35-36

THERE ARE MANY KINDS of convalescent diets, diets prescribed to allow one to convalesce or heal. Convalescent and convalesce aren't words we typically use these days. It likely has a lot to do with the fact that we don't really think much about rest and recovery. Rest is short-lived and rare, like a vacation. Recovery is very nearly absent. We are sick or injured, and then we demand that we are not and expect of ourselves and others an immediate return to life as it was before, as if our bodies don't need time to rebuild and restore. Our bodies can only serve us well if we serve them well, and the modern pressures demand so much of us that we so willingly give; there is little left for ourselves.

To convalesce means to intentionally withdraw to some degree or another and devote some of our energies to serving our own bodies. Sometimes we do so to prevent a worsening of symptoms or conditions, and at other times, there is simply no choice; we are unable to do anything else. One of the ways that we can encourage and support others who do this work is by extending hospitality to them at this time, to give them the opportunity that they need to restore their health and strength. We have as our best example the biblical case of the Good Samaritan in Luke 10:25-37.

In the parable, a man was attacked and beaten by highway bandits and left for dead at the side of the road. More than one fine, respectable, even well-meaning person walked past this poor man as he lay there alone and unable to care for himself. They all had good reasons, ones that are actually defensible. The priest who passed him likely assumed he was dead and did not stop to check because, if he had, he would have been unable to serve in the temple. The Levite also passed him, a man from the tribe who was devoted to religious service. The Jews had restrictions about touching blood and if this man was bloody, he could not have touched him without necessitating a religious bath. They did not necessarily have any ill will, but in the end, they both failed to serve their fellow man in his moment of need.

Ultimately, it was the Samaritan who stopped and checked on this man. The Samaritan would not have garnered much respect in that time and place; in fact, Samaritans were shunned and, in some cases, openly reviled. It was this reviled man who stopped and offered hospitality, encouragement, and hope. The brutalized man needed his wounds washed and treated and bandaged. He needed an opportunity to rest in a safe and secure place, with someone to bring him food and drink and perhaps additional medicine. Without this hospitality, he could not have hoped to convalesce. He would have died where he lay on the side of the road, either from exposure or from his untreated injuries.

The Samaritan carried this man on his own donkey to an inn where he cared for him and charged the innkeeper with the task of continuing in his stead after he had gone. The Samaritan promised to repay whatever he spent above and beyond what was given him initially.

My husband serves as a married priest attached to a small monastery, and he gives a weekly homily at the Sunday liturgy for the parishioners of the mission facilitated by the monastery. Recently he gave a homily on this passage wherein he encouraged our parishioners to remember who they are in this, and every parable.

We are not the hero of the story. It is far too tempting to see ourselves this way, but that is not who we are. We are not the Samaritan who carries this man to the Inn. We are not the innkeeper or even the inn itself. Christ is the Samaritan, the one we rejected but who comes to save us. The inn is the Church that Christ founded and gives to us as a shelter from the dangers of the highway. The innkeeper is the priest who anoints us and communes us and saves us from the death of sin when he hears our confessions.

We are broken people making broken decisions. Our decisions are often rational, and we believe they are defensible even when they aren't. Sometimes we are the victim of the highway bandits, the one who was overtaken on the highway and robbed, our souls bloodied with sin. Often, we are instead those who passed by him. We are the ones who saw his broken and battered body and chose to look away and instead fix our gaze on another city. The sad thing is that the inn is near, and we fail to see it for what it is.

Christ is in our midst.
He is and ever shall be.

These are the words that brother priests use to greet each other in the altar during the Divine Liturgy. As fellow innkeepers serving in the inn at the command of the Good Samaritan, they remind themselves just Whom they serve.

We don't have to be priests in the altar to serve our fellow man. Christ gives us the command to go out and do the same, to serve Him in the ways that we can. The world is full of opportunities to provide hospitality. The work that we do to provide hospitality and care to the convalescent is holy work, work that God has repeatedly asked us to do. He reminds us when He tells us about the Good Samaritan, and He further encourages us by reminding us that when we do these things, we serve Him.

I am profoundly grateful for the benevolence of God Who loves His creatures so much that our service to others pleases Him so greatly. It makes me think of the way in which I love my own children so fiercely. If that were my son or daughter, naked and bleeding and frightened, I could think of no greater thing that someone could do for me than to rescue my child. There would be no human limit to my gratitude; but even then, my gratitude would be limited as is my love for my children, because I am limited. A finite creature can only love in a finite way, can only feel gratitude in a finite way, but God is infinite. God's love is infinite. When we care for His children, the ones He loves infinitely, it pleases Him so greatly, and it is this that brings us closer to Him. What a beautiful thing that we are able to do! We should be grateful to the person we care for, because they give us this opportunity to love God a little better.

One of the ways that we can enter into this mutual relationship is by preparing food for others while they convalesce. Knowing exactly what kind of food to serve them can be complicated, and so it is important to talk about different convalescent diets and why patients are on them and what they can and cannot eat. Once we know this, then we can properly feed them.

CLEAR LIQUID DIET

This is the most restrictive of all the convalescent diets and largely includes liquids, but they do not necessarily have to be clear, despite the name. Liquids should be transparent even if tinted and with no solid bits. Because gelatin is liquid at room temperature, it is allowed so long as it has no pulp or added ingredients. It is called a clear liquid diet because this is usually a good explanation to help guide our understanding of the diet, which is mostly clear and mostly liquid. This is usually followed only for brief periods of time, say before lower gastrointestinal or GI procedures like a colonoscopy. In this case, the goal of the diet is to prevent any residue or undigested food waste to pass from the stomach into the intestines. It can also be given following surgeries of the mouth or throat like a tonsillectomy in order to allow incisions to begin to heal. Sometimes this diet is prescribed for a very short period in order to help a person recover from nausea and vomiting.

Severely limiting the sorts of food and drink that someone consumes can allow the stomach to rest and recover from acute illnesses. Because the diet is so restricted, it can be incredibly problematic for diabetics, and it is best to consult with a dietician to determine what and especially when to drink and eat. It is critical for most diabetics to consume a total of 200 grams of carbohydrates over the course of each day, and it must be very carefully spaced out[1] to maintain a consistent blood glucose level. Diabetics should transition to a full liquid diet as soon as possible.

It is important to note that in the case of recent surgeries or injuries that low acid foods are preferred. If there is a chance of bleeding, red-colored foods should be avoided. They can be confused for blood or disguise it, which is not helpful when monitoring a loved one following a medical procedure. Because this is the most restrictive diet, it is usually easier to think of what is permitted rather than what it is not, though it is important to add that dairy in all forms is disallowed.

It is important to note that carbonated drinks are not recommended for patients following some surgeries because they can increase pain and discomfort[2]. Laparoscopic surgeries require filling the abdomen with gas to provide room to work, and this has to dissipate through the body. Adding more gas can make moving this gas even more uncomfortable. Mouth and throat surgeries can mean that there are other

---

[1] Accessed on 6/15/21 https://www.mayoclinic.org/healthy-lifestyle/nutrition-and-healthy-eating/in-depth/clear-liquid-diet/art-20048505
https://www.pihhealth.org/app/files/public/869487cd-3a1c-44d2-a952-37590f687bdf/colonoscopy-instructions-4-14-17-v1.pdf
[2] Accessed on 11/3/21
https://www.uchealth.com/services/colon-rectal-surgery/patient-information/what-to-expect-after-laparoscopic-surgery/

restrictions such as not using a straw because of the internal pressure it can cause on healing tissues[3]. This can also extend to sucking on hard candies, so it is important to check your loved one's discharge papers to be certain what is and what is not allowed.

Clear Liquid Diet Foods and Beverages	
Water, with or without flavoring perhaps carbonated*	Popsicles with no fruit, dairy, nuts, seeds**
Fruit juices with no pulp such as apple*, white grape*, cranberry**	Gelatins, with no fruit, vegetables, or dairy*
Fruit flavored punch**	Sweeteners like honey, sugar*
Lemonade, limeade	Sports drinks*
Bone broth, strained and fat-free*	Energy drinks with no dairy
Electrolyte	Hard candies* (not

---

[3] Accessed on 11/03/21
https://oralsurgeryomaha.com/patients/post-op-instructions.html#:~:text=Avoid%20using%20a%20straw%2C%20sucking.likelihood%20of%20a%20dry%20socket.&text=Maintaining%20good%20hygiene%20is%20especially.site(s)%20are%20healing.

replacement drinks*	appropriate for all patients)
Broth that is thoroughly strained	Coffee and tea, including herbal varieties but avoid medicinal types
Aspic, strained broth set with gelatin	
*Low acid options **Avoid red foods following surgery or injury	

Because this diet is very low in calories and nutrition, generally, it is a very short-term diet. But even then, it can be extremely frustrating and can lead to hunger and low energy. Try sitting down with your loved one while they drink and eat, and try to provide meals, even though they consist of beverages and gelatins, three times a day plus snacks between. It is important to provide enough sugars to maintain energy, so be sure that there is a food that provides some carbohydrates. Your loved one might be very cranky, and it is important to remember that whatever frustrations they express, they are not personal. It is cold comfort, but remember that it is the hunger and frustration talking. Ultimately, it is not about you. Avoiding eating around your loved one can help minimize their frustrations and thereby yours.

Breakfast, lunch, and dinner could consist of a bowl of well-strained broth and some gelatin as well as a beverage. Snacks between meals and one before bed will help with blood sugar levels and might include a popsicle or granita and another beverage. Granita is a flaky kind of frozen dessert that is similar to but not exactly like shaved ice. Usually, it is made with whole fruit but it is possible to make it with juice, which makes it appropriate for a clear liquid diet. It takes a while to prepare but isn't challenging. Make this in advance so that you don't have to do it with a cranky, hungry loved one waiting on you.

Prepare for this brief period by preparing or purchasing a mix of all allowed foods and beverages, avoiding higher acid foods as well as red if you have been asked to do so. Make a batch of bone broth, but keep in mind that someone on a clear diet will drink about a quart a day, if not more. It is worthwhile to prepare a couple of batches of granita. This is helpful in avoiding not just the artificial colors and flavors of store-bought ice desserts but also the solid fruit which can't be eaten on this diet. Traditionally, granita is made with pureed whole fruit and not just the juice. You can also use the granita base in homemade popsicle molds. A batch or two of flavored simple syrup can be added to water, tea, or coffee and add some appealing flavor as well as a boost of sugar when there is little nutrition.

This period is short but deeply frustrating, so be patient with your loved one and especially with yourself. Encourage your loved one to rest while on the diet and to go to bed early the night before the procedure, and it would be helpful for you to follow suit. This will be over soon, even if it does not feel like it is soon enough.

Remember that recovering from a clear liquid diet might take some time. Your medical provider might recommend transitioning to a full liquid diet or a puree diet first, so be sure to follow those instructions. The digestive system does not like to be shocked, and moving backward in terms of allowed foods can feel devastating. It is best to avoid it.

APPROPRIATE RECIPES FOR THIS DIET:
- Bone Broth
- Basic Fruit Gelatin
- Basic Aspic
- Herb-Infused Simple Syrup
- Spiced Simple Syrup
- Simple Iced Tea by the Pitcher
- Russian Style Tea by the Pitcher
- Lemonade
- Mulled Apple Juice
- Fruit Juice Granita

FULL LIQUID DIET

The full liquid diet is less restrictive than the clear and is usually a transition to a mechanical soft or pureed diet. This diet might be prescribed to the patient following surgery or injury to the mouth, throat, or stomach as well as other interventions. This diet allows the patient to have a broader diet but still allows the mouth, throat, stomach, and intestines to rest because it is specifically a low strain on the gastrointestinal system.

If you are feeding a convalescent on this diet, they will need to eat more often than the typical three-square-meals-a-day manner that most of us eat. This is because smaller amounts of food are usually eaten at a time and they are less nutritionally dense than solid foods. Most people on this diet will need to eat six to eight times a day. It is important to offer them something at your meal times but also between each meal and the next and perhaps again before retiring for the night. If they are taking pain medication which often needs to be taken with food to prevent upsetting the stomach, middle-of-the-night doses are challenging. Because many pain medications should be taken with food to prevent nausea, having a snack prepared beforehand is helpful. It is also a good idea to have that medication dosed and ready to go because it is more difficult to measure carefully when you are already so tired. Be patient with your loved ones as they take their medication because they might need to take it in a few swallows. When the body is healing, swallowing is a lot of effort.

This diet includes everything allowed on the clear diet with a few additional foods. Two of the major differences between a clear versus full-liquid diet is the inclusion of dairy back into the diet and the addition of scrambled eggs. Scrambled eggs, particularly if gently and lightly cooked to prevent them from becoming rubbery, are a welcome source of semi-solid food and are a safe addition[4] because they are high in water. Again, in the case of a recent mouth surgery, your care instructions might be to avoid chewing and eggs would not be a safe option until the site is better healed. Always follow your specific care instructions.

Generally speaking, this diet includes all beverages and foods that will become liquid at room temperature or are of high water content. Fats can be added to the diet unless gastrointestinal issues preclude it. It is important to note that in the instance of recent surgery, low acid foods are still recommended and red-colored foods are still to be avoided.

If you are caring for someone with recent throat surgery, like a tonsillectomy, often surgeons recommend avoiding dairy for the first

---

[4] Accessed on 6/29/21
https://www.stmaryshealthcaresystem.org/health-and-wellness/nutrition/special-diets

several days. When my daughter had hers removed, she found it aggravated her mucus over the surgical site, something the doctor told us might happen. The common advice to feed her ice cream was not appropriate and she was sad about that. Instead, we gave her lots of sorbet and sherbet, both of which are either light on the dairy or dairy-free, and this worked better for her. We did avoid high acid options like lemon and anything red and she readily transitioned to the mechanical soft diet.

Full Liquid Diet Foods and Beverages	
Water, plain or carbonated with or without flavoring*	Popsicles with no fruit, dairy, nuts, seeds*
Fruit juices, strained with no pulp such as apple, grape, cranberry*	Gelatins, with no fruit, vegetables, or dairy*
Fruit flavored punch*	Sweeteners like honey, sugar*
Lemonade, limeade	Sports drinks*
Bone broth, strained*	Energy drinks
Electrolyte replacement drinks*	Hard candies*

Creamed soups with no solids*	Cooked cereals prepared to be thin*
Ice cream with no fruit, nuts, candy*	Yogurt, kefir*
Sorbets, sherbet with no solid fruit	Butter, cream*
Scrambled eggs*	Meal replacement drinks*
Pureed food thin enough to be served with a syringe	
*Low acid options	

The pureed diet section is full of recipes that also work for those on a full liquid diet. When on this diet, remember that the food needs to be thin enough to be served with a syringe. If the food is too thick to be pressed out of one, then it is too thick to eat. Many patients on this diet cannot eat using a straw so be clear with your care provider about whether or not straws are allowed.

One of the most important things to remember for caring for a family member on a full liquid diet is to remember emergency foods. Often patients keep prepared protein drinks on hand for those times when they need to eat but don't have the means to eat. If you use prepared powder, it is a good idea to also keep bottled water on hand. There are many bottles with a variety of tops or balls that make it easier to blend the powder into a smooth beverage. If your loved one can be out and about, be sure to grab some of these every time you leave in case you need to have a quick meal. If you pack everything into a zipper top bag and replace the contents immediately after using it, it will be easy to be prepared.

If your loved one has a feeding tube that is placed in the mouth, nose, or belly, the steps to feeding are complicated and are best discussed with your care provider to be sure that you are feeding properly and safely. Some patients feed through the mouth using a syringe when they are able to accept food but for whatever reason cannot open their mouth easily. In this case, be sure to keep the food thin enough to pass through the syringe and press a small amount at a time not onto the tongue but in the cheek pocket, between the teeth, and check. Allow the patient to swallow before giving them more to eat. This is a slow process so be patient. Try playing music or listening to an audiobook to make this long interaction more pleasant.

If your loved one is using a pump to facilitate bolus feeds, ask if it would be appropriate to use a gravity feed for when you are out and about. It can help to provide more mobility and this could be freeing for the whole family. Sometimes, it is of considerable emotional benefit to be able to provide treats, such as ice cream, even though they can't be enjoyed in the same way. Be sure to be clear with your physician concerning amounts of food to be fed when patients cannot tell us if they are sufficiently full.

APPROPRIATE RECIPES FOR THIS DIET:
- Bone Broth
- Creamed Vegetable Soups (puree and thin with broth until it can be drunk with a straw, even if a straw cannot be used)
- Soupe Alexander (puree and thin with broth until it can be drunk with a straw, even if a straw cannot be used)
- Chicken and Dumpling Soup (puree and thin with broth until it can be drunk with a straw, even if a straw cannot be used)
- Beef and Barley Soup (choice the rice options and puree thin with broth until it can be drunk with a straw, even if a straw cannot be used)
- Creamy Mushroom Soup (puree and thin with broth until it can be drunk with a straw, even if a straw cannot be used)
- Basic Fruit Gelatin
- Basic Creamy Gelatin
- Basic Aspic
- Panna Cotta

- Fruit Smoothies
- Fudge Pops
- Flavored Dairy Coffee Creamer
- Flavored Non-Dairy Coffee Creamer
- Herb-Infused Simple Syrup
- Spiced Simple Syrup
- Simple Iced Tea by the Pitcher
- Russian Style Tea by the Pitcher
- Lemonade
- Mexican Style Hot Chocolate
- Mulling Spices for Apple Juice, Apple Cider, Wine
- Hot Toddy
- Lower Phosphorus White Sauce Mix
- Dairy White Sauce Mix
- Gentle Cooked Cereal
- Rich Cooked Cereal
- Gentle Scrambled Eggs
- Rich Scrambled Eggs
- Berry Compote
- High-Protein Milkshake
- High-Protein Sorbet
- Whipped Cream
- Whipped Coconut Cream
- Coconut Milk Fruit Sorbet
- Fruit Juice Granita (Chipped Ice)
- Homemade Vegetable Purees
- Maple Cinnamon Carrots (puree and thin with broth until it can be drunk with a straw, even if a straw cannot be used)

- Buttered Spiced Beets (puree and thin with broth until it can be drunk with a straw, even if a straw cannot be used)
- Creamed Spinach (puree and thin with broth until it can be drunk with a straw, even if a straw cannot be used)
- Oven Roasted Zucchini (puree and thin with broth until it can be drunk with a straw, even if a straw cannot be used)

MECHANICAL SOFT OR PUREED DIET

This diet is often a transition from a liquid diet to the full diet and is a happy medium between the two. The diet consists of naturally soft foods or ones that have been pureed in order to make them gentle on the mouth and throat when swallowed and require no chewing. The term "mechanically" refers to the mechanical aspects of eating, specifically the physical aspects of using lips, teeth, and throat to eat. These are foods that are soft enough to be easily consumed with no mechanical strain. Even though this diet is largely an adaptation of a regular diet, it can feel more restrictive and unsatisfying because of the limited variety of textures. This makes it very important to offer as widely differing textures as possible to keep the convalescent's attention. Some patients are on this diet permanently and it can take an emotional toll on them. Silicone food molds can allow you to puree foods and serve them shaped like the original. The food will still be pureed but it will initially look more like the familiar food your loved one is missing.

Sometimes people are placed on this diet because they have physical difficulty in chewing or swallowing because of illness, injury, or recent surgery. Other situations can be when someone has lost feeling in parts of their mouth because of injury or recent surgery. It is as important to be gentle to recovering tissues as it is to keep them clean and free of food particles. This diet is specifically designed to meet their needs. This diet is sometimes referred to as a "toddler diet" which makes a lot of sense given that toddlers are developing the skills for eating as well as growing teeth that enable them to properly chew meaning their diet is very similar to a mechanically soft diet. Remember this can be really helpful for thinking about the kinds of foods you are serving and the ways that you will be serving them to your loved one as long they need this diet. Just like a toddler, sometimes your loved one will be able to eat very finely minced or chopped food which can be a welcome treat when the rest of the diet is ground or blended into pastes or thicker liquids. In other cases, foods that can be mashed with a spoon can also be served as is which helps add more variety. The important thing is to offer as much variety as is possible because this nourishes your loved one's emotional health.

One of the struggles for caregivers is trying to find ways of meeting the physical needs of their loved ones with all of the other demands of life. It is not always possible to devote a lot of time to the kitchen. There is no shame in buying prepared fruits and vegetables (such as canned and frozen) or even jarred or frozen baby food meals. There is a surprising number of options for smooth baby food dinners that can provide critical nutrition when caregivers need a break from meal preparation. Adopt that common saying among new parents regarding the feeding of babies and that is, "Fed is best!" When faced with an enormous amount of pressure and strain, it is better to buy some prepared foods than it is for anyone to go hungry or for caregivers to break their spirits. Another way to reduce the workload is to modify the family meal to meet the needs of the patient. See the end of this section to learn how to take the family meals and blend them with bone broth to add moisture and nutrition at the same time as well as how to add a thickener to more liquid food to make them easier to swallow.

Foods to avoid on a pureed diet are those that are dry, crispy, crunchy, or hard as well as peels and seeds that can be harder to swallow. Smoothies can be a great option but they often include peels or seeds which can be lodged in surgical incisions or wounds so be sure to be cautious. Also avoid things like cold cereal, toast, dry baked goods without sauces or gravies to moisten them as well as nuts, crackers, peanut butter, firm fruits like apples, and large pieces of meat or vegetables.

Pureed or Mechanically Soft Diet[5]	
Soft, cooked vegetables without peels	Cooked lean meat, poultry, and fish (minced or ground)
Finely chopped or mashed peeled fruits like peaches, bananas, pears, mangoes, avocado	Pasta dishes, low acid (like macaroni and cheese) if recent surgery or injuries
Peeled citrus fruits (not appropriate for low acid diets) (not appropriate for all diets)	Cooked cereals, oatmeal, farina, grits
Mashed cooked potatoes, sweet potatoes, yams (no	Scrambled eggs (not appropriate for all diets)

---

[5] Accessed on 6/16/21 https://www.mskcc.org/cancer-care/patient-education/pureed-and-mechanical-soft-diets

skin)	
Applesauce	Cooked rice (err on the side of more liquid) (not appropriate for all diets)
Cottage cheese, cream cheese	Soups (as long as the pieces are very small and soft)
Ice cream, sherbet, sorbet	Gravies (some diets require no chunky pieces)
Yogurt, both dairy and non-dairy (some diets will require no mixed fruit)	Pancakes, Waffles (with sauce over to moisten*)
Pudding, custards, gelatin	Bone broth
*Appropriate for mechanically soft but not for puree diets	

When considering what foods are appropriate for your loved one, there are three levels of thickness when it comes to pureed and mechanically soft foods. Some illnesses and injuries require foods to be of a certain consistency whether that is thinner or thicker. Be clear with your care providers about how your loved one must eat. Some conditions will improve with time and it might be possible to add more and more foods as they transition to a fuller and more filling diet.

Levels of Pureed Food Thickness[6]		
Level One	Level Two	Level Three
Pureed until smooth with a consistent texture and no small pieces are present.	All level one foods plus combined texture foods like pasta dishes or meat and vegetable dishes or soups with pieces no larger than ¼ inch (5mm) or so.	All level one and two foods plus others that are soft and moistened with sauces, syrups, and gravies. Foods can be larger but should all be smaller than the bowl of a spoon and should be able to mash with the backside of a spoon. Nothing

---

[6] Accessed on 11/4/21 https://www.healthgrades.com/right-care/digestive-health/mechanical-soft-diet-how-it-works-and-recommended-foods

		sticky or dry is permitted.

If your loved one is unable to swallow liquids that are too thin, you will need to pay attention to the thickness of not just the solid foods but also the liquids in the diet. Some injuries or illnesses mean that patients have difficulty with liquids and require foods to be slightly thicker in order to swallow them effectively without choking. This condition is known as dysphagia. In this case, swallowing can be difficult or painful and can originate in either the mouth or the throat. Some patients will need to use a syringe to eat and drink and some others will be restricted to using an open cup. The cup helps remind patients to not take in too much at any one time to avoid choking. When considering the thickness of a liquid, remember that it is not dependent on its state as it is served but on its melted texture which can be surprising to learn. Some foods we think of as being semi-solid aren't and might not be appropriate for all patients. For instance, gelatin foods are actually nectar thick because they can melt while being consumed and it is the melted state that the sick room cook needs to be concerned with.

Levels of Liquid Thickness[7]			
Spoon Thick	Honey Thick	Nectar Thick	Thin Liquids
Thick enough that it cannot be drunk but must be eaten with a spoon.	Thick enough that it cannot be drunk through a straw but not so thick that it must be eaten with a spoon.	Slightly thicker than water but can easily be drunk with a straw.	The same consistency as water.
Example: Pudding	Example: Thick milkshake	Example: Tomato juice	Example: Coffee or tea

Your doctor might have already ordered a pureed diet and discussed with you the proper thickness levels for the foods your loved one is eating. The medical staff might have also discussed being aware of signs of difficulty in swallowing. Regardless, when your loved one is eating, coughing and choking are obvious signs of

---

[7] Accessed on 11/4/21 http://hdsa.org/wp-content/uploads/2015/02/In-the-Thick-of-it.pdf

trouble swallowing challenges but so are a gurgling sound when speaking during eating and food left in the mouth after swallowing. Excessive drooling while eating or complaints of pain while swallowing can be other indicators. All of these are conditions to bring up with your care provider whether or not they have a previous diagnosis of difficulty. This helps your care provider meet the needs of your loved one.

If you are pureeing foods for your loved one, use a food processor with a sharp blade or a stick blender and add one-quarter cup of liquid for every cup of solid food like casseroles or bread. It is best to heat the liquid first before adding it to the food in order to keep the meal hot. Pureed entrees are best served warm because they feel less like baby food. You can use fruit or vegetable juice, bone broth, vegetable broth, milk, yogurt, or kefir to get the proper consistency. For patients who need more nutritional support, using a meal replacement drink as the liquid can provide even more calories. Some foods, like meats, need more liquid than other foods. Use ⅓ cup of warm liquid for every two to three ounces of meat. If your loved one is eating using a syringe, be sure it is thin enough to pass through the opening[8]. Always test the food's temperature before serving,

---

[8] Accessed on 11/4/21
https://medicine.umich.edu/sites/default/files/content/downloads/meal-planning-soft-diet.pdf

especially if your loved one has a limited ability to tell you if something is not quite right.

Pureeing Casseroles, Pies, and Cobblers	Pureeing Breads and Rolls	Pureeing Meats, Sausages, Patties, Fish
¼ cup of liquid for every cup of food, process or blend with a warm liquid until smooth	¼ cup of liquid (milk works very well) per cup of lightly compressed bread, consider molding and serving as a pudding	⅓ cup of liquid for meat, process or blend with warm liquid until smooth (remove sausage casing first)

Dysphagia aside, there are other reasons to keep some liquids thicker. Some patients can swallow well but need food thickened to make self-feeding easier because liquid foods tend to slip off the spoon. While there are a lot of commercial thickening products on the market, all of which work well, they are not readily available in the grocery store. It can be helpful to know that xanthan gum, an ingredient often used in gluten-free baking, can be found in bulk in most stores. It is fairly expensive but it is used in very tiny amounts in thickening foods so you only need to buy small amounts.

One of the benefits of xanthan gum over gelatin and guar gum is that it maintains its structure when heated. This allows you to prepare larger amounts of food at a single time and warm them later for serving. It also allows for more variety in the temperature at which the food is served. When all the food is the same texture, any variation can be a welcome change. Xanthan gum is a fruit sugar so in very high amounts will cause loose stools just like too much fruit will but given the tiny portions used in thickening, this is very unlikely to ever occur. While it is perfectly safe for children and adults, it is not a good additive for baby foods. If you are feeding an infant or toddler with feeding challenges, talk to your medical provider about which thickening product to use. Some thickeners are not compatible with breast milk and using too much greatly increases the risk of choking. The same is true for those on a low residue diet who need to limit fermenting sugars in the GI tract, talk to your care providers to make sure this will be safe for them. It is a good rule of thumb to trust your instincts and ask questions when you have concerns or doubts.

Thickening Liquids	Thickening Purees
⅛ teaspoon of	1/16 - ⅛ teaspoon of

xanthan gum per cup of liquid	xanthan gum per cup of puree food

Using xanthan gum can take a few attempts to get used to because it gels almost immediately. A good tip is to keep the liquid moving quickly and rather than blending by hand, use a blender or stick blender to ensure that it combines thoroughly and quickly. For every cup of liquid to be thickened, start with ⅛ of a teaspoon and combine using a blender, this very quickly incorporates the thickener and evenly distributes it. Continue to blend until it begins to thicken. If trying to firm a puree, start with a pinch or about 1/16th of a teaspoon added per cup and blend using a blender or a stick blender. Keep blending until it begins to thicken. You might need to add additional thickener (1/16th of a teaspoon at a time) until it is at the thickness your provider recommends. Check the chart below to help you gauge the thickness.

If you need to follow this diet for a significant length of time, a stick blender with a cup is a good investment. Often people will ask how they can help and it is hard to know how to accept help when the diet is so limited. Asking for a stick blender is a way to get the help you need to feed your loved one and not have to explain the complexities of the diet.

Levels of Liquid Thickness[9]			
Spoon Thick	Honey Thick	Nectar Thick	Thin Liquids
Thick enough that it cannot be drunk but must be eaten with a spoon.	Thick enough that it cannot be easily drunk through a straw but not so thick that it must be eaten with a spoon.	Slightly thicker than water but can easily be drunk with a straw.	The same consistency as water.
Example: Pudding	Example: Thick milkshake	Example: Tomato juice, gelatins	Example: Coffee or tea

Making purees in bulk and freezing in smaller portions can help the caregiver consolidate the cooking effort. Depending on the ability of your loved one to eat, you can freeze in portions as small as ice cube trays or larger such as mini-

---

[9] Accessed on 11/4/21 http://hdsa.org/wp-content/uploads/2015/02/In-the-Thick-of-it.pdf

muffin trays, or even larger such as regular muffin trays. You can buy medical-grade silicone food molds that look like regular foods but they are pricey. They are worth the cost for those who will be on this diet long-term because it does so much to improve their eating experience. It is also helpful to buy silicone ice cube molds in fun shapes. These are especially helpful for children. If you will be freezing portions for later, be sure to add a source of fat to the puree. That fat allows the puree to remain creamy after freezing plus it provides additional calories needed for recovery. The French have made an art of making enriched purees as a part of their haute cuisine and incorporating this into meal prep for a convalescent can add depth and flavor to meals while supplying necessary nutrition. Despite its fancy attitude, it is not harder than standard mashed potatoes.

An important note is that this diet is low in fiber or roughage, so it can lead to constipation. If this happens, make sure that the convalescent is drinking plenty of liquids. Speak to your provider about adding in high fiber, soft foods like whole-grain cooked cereals such as oatmeal.

APPROPRIATE RECIPES FOR THIS DIET:
- Bone Broth
- Creamed Vegetable Soups
- Soupe Alexander

- Chicken and Dumpling Soup, pureed if necessary
- Beef and Barley Soup, choose rice option and pureed if necessary
- Creamy Mushroom Soup, pureed if necessary
- Sopa de Arroz (Mexican Rice Soup)
- Basic Fruit Gelatin
- Basic Creamy Gelatin
- Basic Aspic
- Panna Cotta (Cream Gelatin)
- Fruit Smoothies
- Molded Salmon Salad
- Fudge Pops
- Flavored Dairy Coffee Creamer
- Flavored Non-Dairy Coffee Creamer
- Herb-Infused Simple Syrup
- Spiced Simple Syrup
- Simple Iced Tea by the Pitcher
- Russian Style Tea by the Pitcher
- Lemonade
- Mexican Style Hot Chocolate
- Mulling Spices for Apple Juice, Apple Cider, Wine
- Hot Toddy
- Lower Phosphorus White Sauce Mix
- Dairy White Sauce Mix
- Gentle Cooked Cereal
- Rich Cooked Cereal
- Gentle Scrambled Eggs
- Rich Scrambled Eggs

- Easy Macaroni and Cheese, pureed if necessary
- Mini Meatloaves, perhaps purees with broth
- Chicken Salad Spread
- Watched Pot Hard-Boiled Eggs, mashed for the puree diet
- Easy Oven Baked Hard-Cooked Eggs, mashed for the puree diet
- Egg Salad
- Berry Compote
- High-Protein Milkshake
- High-Protein Sorbet
- Whipped Cream
- Whipped Coconut Cream
- Coconut Milk Fruit Sorbet
- Fruit Juice Granita (Chipped Ice)
- Homemade Vegetable Purees
- Maple Cinnamon Carrots
- Buttered Spiced Beets, pureed if necessary
- Creamed Spinach, purred if necessary
- Oven Roasted Zucchini, peeled and mashed or pureed if necessary

GASTROINTESTINAL SOFT DIET

A gastrointestinal or GI soft diet is designed to be gentle specifically on the digestive system, rather than easier for the physical aspects of eating but is often helpful for both. It is also a lower residue diet, meaning it reduces the amount of residue that passes into the intestines, but it is not as low as the Low Residue Diet. This means that it will reduce the number and amount of bowel movements[10]. Sometimes this diet is called a bland diet because the foods on this diet are soft, low fiber, low fat, bland, and not overly stimulating which allows the digestive system to rest because of illness, injury, or recent surgeries. It is low acid which can decrease reflux symptoms and give the throat a chance to recover from illness or injury. Sometimes people follow this diet for a very short period as a way of dealing with acute nausea and diarrhea following a bout with a virus or other infection. The gentle nature of the diet and the method of eating can prevent over-stimulation that can trigger more nausea or diarrhea. Often this diet is called the BRAT diet because the names of some of the central allowed foods can create the acronym.

- Bananas
- Rice
- Applesauce
- Toast

While these foods are not the sum total of the foods allowed, it is an easy word to remember, which can help when considering what foods to serve someone on this diet. Learning how to safely and properly feed a convalescing loved one can be

[10] National Center for Biotechnology Information, Bland Diets, accessed on 11/12/21
https://www.ncbi.nlm.nih.gov/books/NBK538142/

overwhelming. Anything that can make this easier is good.

Because the goal is to prevent strain on the digestive system, difficult to digest raw foods and those high in fiber are avoided. Foods that are very hot or are very cold can be shocking to the system and not appropriate for all patients. For many patients, it helps to have food diced or even minced because smaller pieces are able to be digested more quickly and with less effort. The fact that the manner of eating and serving is a critical part of the diet can be one of the more complicated aspects. Some foods are allowed but only when minced or even ground, otherwise they could take too long to digest and create strain on the digestive system or cause difficulty in elimination. For instance, whole nuts are not allowed, and neither is crunchy peanut butter though creamed nuts are allowed. Caffeine is not allowed and neither is decaf coffee because they are both too high in acid. Decaffeinated teas are permitted because they are low in acid. For this diet, the acid level of the food or drink is as important as its texture. It is important to be careful about these kinds of distinctions to keep your loved one's healing on track.

Another challenge is that the food is necessarily bland, which can make it unappealing. Because it is low in fiber, it can also lead to constipation making it important to encourage the patient to drink lots of water, which can help mitigate this. Try to provide as much texture and flavor variation as is possible, for instance, toasting white bread to add a crunchy mouthfeel in the absence of other textures. Broiling food can also give an interesting texture when much of the food is boiled or baked and often mashed. Grilling and poaching are other ways of preparing food that can provide an interesting twist while on this diet. Toasting white rice in a dry pan before adding the cooking liquid adds a rich, nutty flavor without adding stimulating spices or ingredients. Another helpful trick is to cook soups and rice using whole pieces of onion and garlic that flavor the food but are fairly easy to pull out before serving to prevent digestion difficulties. Try piercing these foods with a toothpick to make them even easier to remove. Sachets used to hold herbs in cooking are even easier to remove, which allows smaller-sized pieces of garlic and onion to be used in cooking. Smaller pieces will transfer flavor better making this an ideal way to add flavor without compromising digestion.

Cinnamon is allowed on this diet, as is ginger, both of which can add more variety when so many other spices are not appropriate. This is especially important to note for patients who miss spicy foods because they are not able to have chiles or even pepper in their food. Patients will often miss fresh fruits but gelatins can be a refreshing alternative to applesauce and other pureed fruits. Try molding pureed fruit to look more like the original. Silicon molds are easy to find online and can make meals more appealing. See the Appealing Meals section for more suggestions. Fresh fruit can be added to drinking water to give it flavor even though the fresh fruit can't be eaten but still avoid citrus fruits because they are acidic. This is a good time to experiment with herbal teas drunk both warm and cool (though not often iced) since caffeine and bubbly drinks aren't allowed. Some patients are on this diet for longer periods of time and finding creative ways to make it more pleasant can help them to be compliant with their doctor's instructions.

Some aspects of the diet aren't related to the food itself but how it's consumed. On this diet, it is important to try to eat smaller meals, more often. This prevents putting periods of big strain on the digestive organs. Try serving three smaller meals with a snack in the morning and afternoon. Encourage the patient to eat slowly and chew thoroughly. A very tired person should only recline but not lay down immediately after eating, and stopping foods three hours before bed in the evening are both helpful in preventing reflux. Patients should also avoid using a straw because it can trap air in the belly which increases gas and discomfort. On this diet, it is critical to drink enough water to prevent constipation and to make it easier to digest. Patients should drink enough that their urine is pale, this is a good sign that they are drinking enough[11].

The labor involved in caring for a loved one can be extraordinary. Choosing easy-to-serve options like canned vegetables or baby food purees can free up time for other needs. There is only so much time in a day and caregivers have a lot of needs to consider. There should be no shame and certainly, no one should ever be criticized or unfairly judged for using these foods.

GI Soft Foods[1213]		
Refined white flour bread, pasta, crackers	Squash, peeled, zucchini roasted, steamed, frozen	Eggs, boiled (hard or soft), scrambled (not fried)
White rice	Applesauce	Tofu
Tender (not	Cooked	Aspics

[11] Crohn's and Colitis Foundation brochure titled "Diet, Nutrition, and Inflammatory Bowel Disease), accessed on 6/15/21 https://www.crohnscolitisfoundation.org/sites/default/files/20 20-03/diet-and-nutrition-brochure.pdf
[12] The Children's Hospital of the King's Daughters, Bland Diets, accessed on 11/12/21 https://www.chkd.org/patients-and-families/health-library/way-to-grow/bland-diet/

[13] Accessed on 12/23/21 https://my.clevelandclinic.org/health/articles/15637-gastrointestinal-soft-diet-overview

fibrous) beef, chicken with fat and gristle removed	cereals, farina, cream of wheat	
Smooth nut butters, no small pieces	Watermelon, cantaloupe, honeydew	Pudding, custard
Cinnamon	Cucumber, peeled	Gelatin
White or yellow potatoes, boiled, mashed, or baked or canned (no skins)	Peeled ripe fruits like bananas, pears, peaches (fresh, frozen, baby food varieties all work)	Avocados (not appropriate for all patients because of fat and fiber)
Carrots, peeled, boiled, mashed, steamed, canned, frozen	Fruit water (though the fruit should not be eaten and no citrus fruits are allowed)	Zucchini, peeled and well cooked
Peas, boiled, steamed,	Mayonnaise*	Low fat dairy such as

canned, frozen		yogurt, kefir*
Herbal teas	Spinach (cooked, canned, or frozen)	Green beans, wax beans (cooked, canned, or frozen)
Skinless hot dogs, Vienna sausages**	Sausage patties (mild seasoning)	Lunchmeat with no whole spices
Ice cream, sherbet	Cottage cheese	Pretzels, white flour
Chips with mild seasonings**	Jelly, no seeds and no whole fruit spreads	Refined and enriched cold cereals with no nuts, berries, dried fruit
Marshmallows	Fish	
*Some diets require low-fat versions **Not appropriate for mechanically soft diets		

This diet is more restrictive than the mechanically soft diet. One of the key distinctions between the mechanically soft diet and the GI soft diet is the lowered presence of fat, even healthy fats. Many fatty foods like full-fat dairy and mayonnaise are soft and easy to chew and swallow, which makes them safe for mechanically soft diets, but fat requires a lot of enzymes and physical effort in order to digest, which makes them inappropriate for the GI soft diet. Low-fat dairy products and low-fat spreads like mayonnaise are usually better options for this diet.

Canned meats are an important tool in the toolbox for those caring for convalescents. The suggestion of canned meat might initially give you pause, we tend to think of canned meats as being a lesser quality food. When we are caring for someone that we love very much, the idea of serving subpar food is deeply concerning. It is important to remember that the need for high-quality, rich sources of protein is increased at times of stress, illness, and injury and the ease of serving canned meat options can be extraordinarily helpful to the caregiver. What is more, often foods like canned meat and Vienna sausages are appealing and it takes less convincing for many patients to eat these foods. Having canned meats as a resource for an overworked sickroom cook can leave more time for other important tasks including caregiver respite.

While it is true that these foods have significant sodium which some patients must restrict, specifically some kidney patients, it is also true that some patients need a great deal of sodium. Sodium is a necessary electrolyte and plays multiple critical roles in our bodies. Illness and injury can deplete sodium which means that we need to serve additional amounts. A short-term example of this need is vomiting which depletes all kinds of electrolytes and fluids. A long-term example of this would be Cystic Fibrosis which causes significant digestion issues and challenges to nutrient absorption. The needs of those coping with illness and injury are very different from healthy and abled people and it is important to keep this in mind while we prepare food for them.

Foods to Avoid on a GI Soft Diet		
Spicy or highly seasoned foods (curry)	Onions, garlic	Whipped cream, sour cream, butter (for some patients)
Hot sauce, spicy peppers	Full fat mayonnaise	Fried foods
Tough, fibrous meats like beef jerky	Sugary foods like candy, sweet baked goods	Caffeine (dehydrating)
No vegetables other than listed, even if	Fresh, raw, frozen fruit	Cereals, breads, crackers, or

cooked		pastas with more than 5g fiber per serving
Chocolate	Popcorn, popcorn cakes, rice cakes	Corn, taco chips
Beans, whole nuts, seeds, chunky nut butter	Spicy sauces like salsa or BBQ	Acidic juice like orange, pineapple, cranberry, lemonade, limeade
Citrus fruits	Pickled vegetables, olives, sauerkraut, pickles	No raw vegetables
Broccoli, cauliflower, Brussel sprouts, beets (can cause gas)	Berries	Pepper. peppercorns
Cloves	Horseradish	Tomato*

Carbonated drinks* (some patients may tolerate ginger ale or lemon-lime soda)	Dried fruit	Mustard
Tea	Mint	Cumin
Nutmeg	Alcohol	Salad dressings (no fats and no vinegar)
*Might be appropriate for some patients		

Some people follow this diet when they have a flare or an increase in symptoms caused by Colitis, Crohn's disease, or other similar conditions. People with these conditions go through periods of being able to eat an almost totally normal diet unless they have a stoma or stricture, and other periods of managing a flare the best that they can with significant dietary changes. One of the special considerations for these patients is that they often must avoid dairy completely so be clear with your medical provider on this. These patients also need a low-sugar diet because it ferments in the gut, this also excludes naturally occurring sugars such as those in fruit juice. This does not mean that they can have sugar substitutes because so many include sugar alcohols. These also readily ferment and can cause all kinds of trouble.

Sugar Alcohol Ingredients to Look For		
xylitol	sorbitol	maltitol
erythritol	mannitol	lactitol
isomalt	hydrogenated starch hydrolysates	

Stevia is an alternative sweetener that does not contain sugar alcohols by itself but is often blended with them, so be sure to check the label. Monk fruit sweetener is also not a sugar alcohol but, like stevia, is often blended with them to improve texture and flavor. When choosing alternatives to sugar, it is important to check labels carefully. It is likely better to learn to eat without them rather than risk problems.

APPROPRIATE RECIPES FOR THIS DIET:
- Bone Broth
- Creamed Vegetable Soups
- Soupe Alexander
- Chicken and Dumpling Soup, remove garlic and onion
- Beef and Barley Soup, use rice option and remove the garlic and onion
- Creamy Mushroom Soup

- Sopa de Arroz (Mexican Rice Soup), omit tomato paste, if necessary
- Basic Fruit Gelatin
- Fruit Studded Gelatin, choose canned peaches and fruit cocktail
- Basic Aspic
- Panna Cotta (Cream Gelatin), low-fat version
- Fruit Smoothies, choose frozen bananas or peaches
- Molded Salmon Salad
- Fudge Pops
- Flavored Dairy Coffee Creamer
- Flavored Non-Dairy Coffee Creamer
- Herb-Infused Simple Syrup
- Spiced Simple Syrup
- Simple Iced Tea by the Pitcher, choose decaf teas
- Russian Style Tea by the Pitcher, choose decaf teas
- Lemonade
- Mexican Style Hot Chocolate, use low-fat milk
- Mulling Spices for Apple Juice, Apple Cider, Wine
- Hot Toddy, choose decaf teas
- Lower Phosphorus White Sauce Mix
- Dairy White Sauce Mix
- Gentle Cooked Cereal
- Gentle Scrambled Eggs
- Easy Macaroni and Cheese, low-fat version

- Mini Meatloaves
- Chicken Salad Spread
- Watched Pot Hard-Boiled Eggs
- Easy Oven Baked Hard-Cooked Eggs
- Egg Salad, low fat version
- Berry Compote
- High-Protein Milkshake
- High-Protein Sorbet
- Fruit Juice Granita (Chipped Ice)
- Homemade Vegetable Purees
- Maple Cinnamon Carrots
- Buttered Spiced Beets
- Creamed Spinach
- Oven Roasted Zucchini, peeled

LOW RESIDUE DIET

A low residue diet is one that is designed to greatly reduce the amount of undigested food that enters the intestines from the stomach. This is done to reduce the weight and number of bowel movements. A doctor may prescribe this diet for any number of injuries or illnesses or surgery because this can allow the intestines to rest from the work of digestion and elimination and to make bowel movements less painful, for instance, before a colonoscopy. This diet is helpful for managing the symptoms of inflammatory bowel disease and other conditions but won't resolve the underlying condition causing the symptoms. It can be a short-term measure that gives time for other treatment measures to take effect. Because the diet is so limited, it is important to take a daily multivitamin if the diet is followed for more than two weeks.

A low residue diet limits daily fiber intake to 10-15 grams a day. Fiber cannot be digested and passes into the intestines where it stimulates bowel activity and adds to the bulk of the bowel waste. This means that all sources of fiber have to be considered and limited. This means that even if a fruit or vegetable is considered allowed, no peels of fruits or vegetables are allowed. Milk products are only sometimes allowed. Depending on other conditions, sometimes no dairy is permitted so it is important to be clear with your loved one's medical provider about these restrictions. If you are not able to serve yogurt, talk to the provider also about adding a probiotic supplement to help with the unpleasant side effect of constipation that can result from a low fiber diet. Drinking lots of water can help with this.

It is also very important to look at the nutrition facts on allowed foods because fiber is often added to a surprising number of mild foods like yogurt and ice cream with no specific labeling. Always check the labels and make sure that there is less than 1-2g per serving but be aware that the listed serving size can also be a little deceptive. If a container of yogurt has two servings but you plan on eating the whole container, you will need to multiply the fiber by the same number of serving as the whole container has. It is also helpful to scan the ingredients list to look for added fiber.

Hidden Sources of Fiber		
Arabinoxylan	Hydroxypropyl-methylcellulose	Resistant starch
Beta-Glucan	Inulin	Resistant dextrin
Carboxymethylcellulose	Modified resistant starch	Resistant maltodextrin
Cellulose	Oligofructose	Rice bran
Chicory root fiber	Pea fiber	Short-chain fructooligosaccharides
Cottonseed fiber	Pectin	Soluble corn fiber
Edible bean powder	Polydextrose	Soluble dextrin
Fructo-oligosaccharides	Polyfructose	Soy fiber
Galacto-oligosaccharides	Psyllium	Wheat bran

Xanthan gum		

Some of the surprising places that you will find added fiber are lower carb versions of foods. Soluble fiber might be added as a way of slowing the absorption of carbohydrates in the bloodstream. Sometimes fiber is added as a way of adding body to low-fat foods. For healthy people with healthy functioning digestive systems, this could be helpful. For those on a low-residue diet, this is dangerous. It is important to check even foods that might seem like a safe option. Yogurt seems like an easy addition to the meal tray, but not this one. See the ingredients list for this particular non-fat, low-carb yogurt:

"Cultured grade A non-fat milk, chicory root fiberwater, contains less than 1% of vegetable juice concentrate (for color), natural flavors, stevia leaf extract, malic acid. Sodium citrate, sea salt, and vitamin D3. Contains active cultures."[14]

The added chicory root fiber might not be an obvious source of fiber, but it is. Without it, the yogurt would have no fiber, but this container has 6g of fiber in each one-cup container. That is too much for this diet, in fact, it is three times as much

---

[14] Accessed on 11/19/21
https://www.danoneawayfromhome.com/food-service-products/dannon-oikos-triple-zero-greek-nonfat-yogurt-2/

fiber as should be included in a single low-residue meal.

This coconut milk ice cream alternative has both chicory root and inulin and both are sources of fiber[15]. A single ⅔ of a cup serving has a whopping 8g of fiber! The container is only a little over ten ounces which is significantly smaller than a pint. If someone ate the entire carton, which would not be very difficult, it would total 24g of fiber which is 1 ½ times the daily fiber limit of this diet:

"Organic coconut milk, water, chicory root fiber, organic erythritol, organic inulin, organic cocoa powder (processed with alkali), organic allulose, guar gum, locust bean gum, stevia"

While one should always be cautious with prepared foods, there are other foods that should be avoided.[16]

Foods to Avoid on a Low-Residue diet	
Whole nuts, chopped nuts	Oatmeal

[15] Accessed on 11/30/21 https://nadamoo.com/products/no-sugar-added-chocolate
[16] Accesse on 11/9/21 https://www.gidoc.md/Education/Low-fiber-residue%20diet%20Education.pdf

Poppyseeds, sesame seeds, caraway seeds	Granola, muesli
Chutney, jams, marmalade, or whole fruit spreads	Shredded wheat
Coconut, shredded or candied	Pseudocereals like chia, quinoa, buckwheat, millet, amaranth
Pineapple	Brown and wild rice
Beans and lentils	Tofu*
Raw or dried fruit, fruit leathers	Cured deli meats
Raw vegetables (unless specifically listed)	Horseradish
Fruit or vegetable peels (even if the food is allowed, remove the peels before cooking)	Relish
Berries	Sauerkraut, kimchi
Whole wheat, whole-grain bread, cereals, crackers, pasta	Pickles
Alcohol*	Popcorn

Caffeine (it can irritate the stomach) *	Broccoli, cauliflower, brussels sprouts
Cabbage, kale, Swiss chard, other "greens"	Prune juice
Onions, garlic	Corn
Plain chocolate	Cloves
Salsa	Limit milk and milk products to 2 cups (16 ounces a day)
Limit high-fat foods	
* Discuss with your doctor as it can cause irritation but might be appropriate in small amounts	

While it feels like an exhausting list of foods to avoid, there are actually a lot of foods to choose from. Make sure to serve as wide a diet as possible to prevent the diet from feeling too restrictive. Usually, the diet is only kept for a short period so try to keep spirits up.

Safe Foods for Low Residue Diets		
Mushrooms	Ketchup	Hard candies
Carrots, peeled before cooking	Mayonnaise	Strained fruit and vegetable juice

Green beans, cooked	Salad dressings (avoid those with seeds)	Caffeine free coffee, tea, sodas
Spinach, cooked	Soy sauce	Bananas
Asparagus, cooked	Maple syrup, honey	Melon
Pumpkin	Clear jellies (avoid whole fruit varieties)	Canned fruit cocktail, peaches
Potatoes, peeled before cooking	Baked goods containing no seeds or nuts	Applesauce
White flour bread, crackers, cereals, pasta with less than 2g of fiber for the amount actually eaten	Ice cream, sherbet, ice milk	Creamed and broth-based soups with pieces of allowed vegetables
Crisped rice or cornflakes cereals	Puddings, Custards	Beets, peeled before cooked
White rice	Pretzels	Fats (as tolerated) including butter,

		margarine, salad oil
Lean, tender meats with fat and gristle removed	Vanilla wafers	Bacon
Eggs (limit fats used in preparation)	Bone broth	Grapes
Alfalfa sprouts	Bell peppers, cooked	Iceberg lettuce
Squash, peeled, cooked	Zucchini, peeled and cooked	Cheese with no nuts
Cottage cheese		

Some of these dietary changes will resolve with treatment or as people move through a flare and are able to transition back to a more or less normal diet. This should always be done slowly with incremental additions of fiber and newly allowed foods in order to prevent strain on the healing digestive system. For some patients, certain changes will persist even with treatment.

Appropriate recipes for this diet:

- Bone Broth
- Creamed Vegetable Soups
- Soupe Alexander
- Chicken and Dumpling Soup
- Beef and Barley Soup, use the rice option
- Creamy Mushroom Soup
- Sopa de Arroz (Mexican Rice Soup), use tomato paste and remove the garlic and onion
- Basic Fruit Gelatin
- Fruit Studded Gelatin, use canned peaches and fruit cocktail
- Basic Aspic
- Kholodets (Studded Aspic), use meat and eggs but no vegetables
- Fruit Smoothies, do not use fruits with seeds
- Molded Salmon Salad
- Fudge Pops
- Flavored Dairy Coffee Creamer
- Flavored Non-Dairy Coffee Creamer
- Herb-Infused Simple Syrup
- Spiced Simple Syrup
- Simple Iced Tea by the Pitcher
- Russian Style Tea by the Pitcher
- Lemonade
- Mexican Style Hot Chocolate, choose low-fat milk

- Mulling Spices for Apple Juice, Apple Cider, Wine
- Hot Toddy
- Lower Phosphorus White Sauce Mix
- Dairy White Sauce Mix
- Gentle Cooked Cereal
- Rich Cooked Cereal
- Gentle Scrambled Eggs
- Rich Scrambled Eggs
- Easy Macaroni and Cheese, use low fat option
- Mini Meatloaves
- Chicken Salad Spread
- Watched Pot Hard-Boiled Eggs
- Easy Oven Baked Hard-Cooked Eggs
- Egg Salad
- High-Protein Milkshake
- High-Protein Sorbet
- Whipped Coconut Cream
- Coconut Milk Fruit Sorbet, do not use fruits with seeds
- Fruit Juice Granita (Chipped Ice)
- Homemade Vegetable Purees
- Maple Cinnamon Carrots
- Buttered Spiced Beets
- Creamed Spinach
- Oven Roasted Zucchini, peeled

RENAL OR KIDNEY DIET

One of the most complicated convalescent diets, if not the most complicated, is a renal diet. Because there are so many moving parts that are dependent on the causes and symptoms of kidney disease, it is very important to be clear with your medical provider about what limitations your loved one will have. Many physicians will refer renal patients to dieticians who specialize in diets for chronic kidney dysfunction. Generally speaking, there are five categories of limitations on the renal diet that might be followed to one degree or another and not all categories will be restricted for all patients.

- Low Liquid
- Low Sodium
- Low Potassium
- Low Phosphorus
- Low Protein

Some patients will need to follow all five restrictions but others will only need to follow a few of these. Because unnecessarily limiting the diet can cause nutritional deficiencies, it is important to only limit the nutrients that your provider has specifically asked you to limit and only to the degree that you have been asked. Excessive restrictions can be dangerous and when someone's health is already fragile, it is especially important to protect it.

It can be confusing to understand why any macronutrients would need to be restricted but it makes more sense when you understand the role of the kidneys in our health. The kidneys perform several critical functions and when they cannot perform them, we modify the diet to reduce the work that they have to do. Because they filter out waste products left in the bloodstream, we reduce the intake of macronutrients to prevent a build-up of these and the additional health conditions that high levels of waste can cause. Patients might be prescribed a renal diet to help slow kidney failure and which might help avoid or delay dialysis though many of these restrictions might continue. Dialysis is a mechanical means of cleansing the blood and while it can preserve health, it is both expensive and time-consuming and not without risks but can be life preserving[17]. Besides removing waste products from the bloodstream, the kidneys also regulate the amount of fluid in the tissues of the body. If the kidneys cannot properly remove this, conditions like edema and swelling can result. Some patients have to severely limit their fluid intake when their kidneys are not able to regulate well.

---

[17] Accessed on 1/12/22
https://www.kidney.org/atoz/content/hemodialysis#can-dialysis-cure-my-kidney-disease

LOW LIQUID DIET

The amount of fluid your loved one will be able to have will depend on the progression of kidney dysfunction[18]. Be clear with the doctor so that your loved one will be able to have the maximum amount permitted. Limiting fluid intake might be the most difficult kidney diet restriction for the caregiver because it's just so counter instinctive. We experience thirst and don't want to deprive others of the means of satisfying it. It is incredibly difficult to deny water to another person. Because it is so hard, the best approach is to prevent thirst as much as possible. Significantly reducing sodium or salt also reduces thirst but given that many chronic kidney disease patients also need to reduce sodium itself, this is akin to killing two birds with one stone. Hard exercise and exposure to heat can also increase thirst, so moderate and consistent exercise is best, and avoid high temperatures.

When your loved one is thirsty, offer sugar-free candies. Sucking on these can help satisfy thirst and moisten the mouth and throat which offers some relief. Rinsing with mouthwash can help if the mouth feels dry but it is important to resist the impulse to swallow. Some patients like to chew gum. It stimulates the production of saliva which also helps a dry mouth.

---

[18] Accessed on 11/22/21 https://kitchen.kidneyfund.org/fluids/

Serving liquids must be done thoughtfully. Don't serve a large mug of water or other beverage to be sipped but instead serve a small amount at a time, perhaps use a smaller glass so it doesn't seem like so little. Drinks without ice avoid the extra liquid but also makes it easier to measure. Alternatively, you can freeze small amounts of liquid in ice cube trays. Sucking on ice can make it last longer and allow a smaller amount of liquid to be more satisfying. Space the allowed amount of liquids consumed throughout the day to avoid long stretches with none, which will be more difficult to manage.

Common Beverages and Liquids to Limit		
Coffee	Coffee creamer	Fruit punch
Tea	Non-dairy substitutes	Meal replacement drinks
Juice	Sparkling water	Alcohol
Soda	Water	Liquid medicines
Milk	Ice	Milkshakes, smoothies

Sports hydration drinks	Electrolyte solutions	

This list is not exhaustive. There are also many foods that include a lot of water that we might not immediately consider. Anything that will become liquid at room temperature as well as any milk, broth, or water used in soups and stews.

Less Obvious Sources of Liquid[19]		
Popsicles	Frozen yogurt	Sauces, gravies
Ice cream, ice milk	Broth	Syrups
Gelatin	Soup	Salad dressing
Sherbet, sorbet	Stews	Some fruits, vegetables
Juice and syrup in canned fruit	Pudding, custard	

Fruits like melons and vegetables like tomatoes and cucumbers have a lot of water and might be

[19] Accessed on 11/22/21 https://www.davita.com/diet-nutrition/articles/basics/food-that-counts-as-fluid-on-the-kidney-diet

limited in this diet. It is a good idea to focus on other, lower liquid options. Kidney friendly, low moisture options include:

Lower Moisture Fruits and Vegetables[20]		
Apples	Celery	Peaches, fresh, not packed in juice
Blackberries	Cherries	Pears, fresh, not packed in juice
Blueberries	Cranberries	Peppers
Broccoli	Cucumbers	Pineapple
Cabbage	Eggplants	Plums
Carrots	Grapes	Strawberries
Cauliflower	Lettuce	Tangerines

LOWER LIQUID RECIPES:
- Easy Macaroni and Cheese
- Mini Meatloaves
- Chicken Salad Spread
- Watched Pot Hard-Boiled Eggs

---

[20] Accessed on 11/22/21 https://www.davita.com/diet-nutrition/articles/basics/food-that-counts-as-fluid-on-the-kidney-diet

- Easy Oven Baked Hard-Cooked Eggs
- Egg Salad
- Maple Cinnamon Carrots
- Buttered Spiced Beets
- Creamed Spinach
- Oven Roasted Zucchini

ELECTROLYTES AND CHRONIC KIDNEY DISEASE

There are three major electrolytes that the body uses[21]. These are sodium, potassium, and chloride, and the first two are often restricted on a renal diet. Electrolytes perform important functions in the body, like regulating our blood pressure, volume, and acid-base balance, as well as managing how much fluid we store in our tissues and causing our muscles to contract.[22] They manage the appropriate amount of the electrolytes we have onboard and when the kidneys are dysfunctional, we might have an excess because they are not excreted properly.

SODIUM REDUCED DIET

Kidney patients are asked to reduce sodium because the inability to excrete excess causes all

---

[21] Accessed pn 11/22/21
https://nephcure.org/livingwithkidneydisease/diet-and-nutrition/renal-diet/
[22] Accessed on 11/22/21
https://www.roswellpark.org/cancertalk/201808/electrolytes-what-are-they-what-happens-if-you-dont-have-enough

kinds of health problems like swelling, breathing difficulty, and even heart failure. One of the easiest ways to reduce sodium in the diet is to take it off the table and to stop cooking using added salt. While this takes getting used to, it goes a long way to reduce the absentminded addition of sodium in the diet. Also, reduce prepared foods as much as is possible. Salt is used in prepared foods to add flavor and because it is a preservative. Caring for a loved one can be a lot of work, and when homemade foods are not an option, look for reduced sodium and salt-free versions. Some patients on a reduced-sodium diet are also on a reduced potassium diet, so it is important to know that many substitutes use this to enhance flavor. It has too much potassium for those who need to restrict this nutrient as well. Avoid salt substitutes and look for naturally salt-free blends and see the recipe section for herb and spice blends that are salt-free.

When checking labels of prepared foods, look at the nutrition facts for sodium. Any ingredients with the word sodium count, even things like sodium nitrite and sodium alginate. Also, look for ingredients with hidden sources of sodium like MSG (monosodium glutamate), baking soda (sodium bicarbonate), and baking powder (which contains baking soda plus an acid). Your doctor might have a different amount of total allowed sodium for your loved one but a good general rule is to make sure that no serving has more than 5% of the recommended daily allowance. Some packaging will account for more than one serving in a container so if you plan on serving the whole amount, be sure to multiply the sodium by the total number of servings in the package.

Choose fresh or frozen vegetables without sauce or seasoning and if using canned, choose no-salt-added options. Canned beans and vegetables can be rinsed under running water to reduce sodium if the regular salted varieties are the only options available.

Foods High in Sodium		
Pizza	Frozen dinners	Cheese
Seasoning blends	Canned soups	Popcorn
Chips, crackers	Nuts (look for unsalted)	Bottled sauces, salad dressing
Canned vegetables	Canned beans	Bouillon cubes, powder
Lunchmeat, sausages, hot dogs, bacon	Canned refrigerated biscuit and dinner rolls	Turkey, chicken with injected

		broth or with solution

One of the surprising sources of sodium in the diet is baked goods, which don't necessarily taste salty but have a significant amount nonetheless. This refrigerated biscuit dough comes in a tube and is baked at home. It contains 20% of the daily allowance of sodium suggested for healthy kidneys and in just one biscuit[23]. If someone has two, which is not an unusual number, it is nearly half the allowance. It is important to check labels and make sure that you are making the best choices possible.

Serving Size: One Biscuit	
Calories	180
Total Fat	6g
Saturated Fat	2.5g
Trans Fat	0g
Cholesterol	0g
Sodium	**450mg**

---

[23] Accessed on 12/21/21
https://www.pillsbury.com/products/biscuits/grands-refrigerated-biscuits/flaky-layers-original

Total Carbohydrate	26g
Dietary Fiber	<1g
Sugars (includes 4g added sugar)	5g
Protein	4g
Iron	1.5mg
Potassium	26mg

RECIPES WITH REDUCED SODIUM OPTIONS:

- Bone Broth
- Creamed Vegetable Soups
- Soupe Alexander
- Chicken and Dumpling Soup
- Beef and Barley Soup
- Creamy Mushroom Soup
- Sopa de Arroz (Mexican Rice Soup)
- Basic Fruit Gelatin
- Basic Creamy Gelatin
- Fruit Studded Gelatin
- Basic Aspic
- Kholodets (Studded Aspic)
- Panna Cotta (Cream Gelatin)
- Fruit Smoothies
- Molded Salmon Salad
- Fudge Pops
- Flavored Dairy Coffee Creamer
- Flavored Non-Dairy Coffee Creamer

- Herb-Infused Simple Syrup
- Spiced Simple Syrup
- Simple Iced Tea by the Pitcher
- Russian Style Tea by the Pitcher
- Lemonade
- Mexican Style Hot Chocolate
- Mulling Spices for Apple Juice, Apple Cider, Wine
- Hot Toddy
- Lower Phosphorus White Sauce Mix
- Dairy White Sauce Mix
- Gentle Cooked Cereal
- Rich Cooked Cereal
- Gentle Scrambled Eggs
- Rich Scrambled Eggs
- Easy Macaroni and Cheese
- Mini Meatloaves
- Chicken Salad Spread
- Watched Pot Hard-Boiled Eggs
- Easy Oven Baked Hard-Cooked Eggs
- Egg Salad
- Berry Compote
- High-Protein Milkshake
- High-Protein Sorbet
- Whipped Cream
- Whipped Coconut Cream
- Coconut Milk Fruit Sorbet
- Fruit Juice Granita (Chipped Ice)
- Homemade Vegetable Purees
- Maple Cinnamon Carrots
- Buttered Spiced Beets

- Creamed Spinach
- Oven Roasted Zucchini

POTASSIUM REDUCED DIET

One of the roles of the kidneys is to keep an appropriate amount of potassium in the body to help with fluid regulation and to keep our heartbeat regular. It is an essential mineral which means that we need it to be healthy but can't produce it ourselves so we have to consume it. It is naturally found in a lot of the foods. Some kidney patients are given potassium binders, often a powder mixed with water and drunk. This binds with the potassium in the foods eaten so that it can be passed in the stool[24].

Almost all foods have potassium but some foods are considered rich sources and others are safer for a potassium reduced diet.

Foods Higher in Potassium[25]

---

[24] Accessed on 12/21/21
https://www.healthline.com/health/high-potassium/potassium-binders#potassium-binders
[25] Accessed on 12/21/21
https://www.kidney.org/atoz/content/potassium
https://www.hsph.harvard.edu/nutritionsource/potassium/
https://www.kidneybuzz.com/surprising-high-in-potassium-foods-that-ckd-and-dialysis-patients-may-be-unknowingly-eating

Pintos, black beans, white beans, peas, lentils	Milk, fortified milk substitutes	Beets
Molasses	Yogurt, cheese	Grapefruit juice
Cantaloupe	Nectarines	Honeydew
Bamboo shoots	Oranges, orange juice (moderate)	Broccoli
Dried apricots, prunes, raisins, dates, figs	Carrots, fresh	Nuts, seeds (peanut butter)
Squash, pumpkin	Most greens (except kale)	Kiwi
Bran, bran flakes	Papaya	Brussel sprouts
Avocados	Mushrooms (moderate)	Chinese or napa cabbage
Artichokes	Okra	Kohlrabi
Chocolate	Rutabagas	Salt substitutes

Bananas	Potatoes, white and sweet (including chips)	Salt-free broth and bullion
Tomatoes	Spinach	Vegetable juice blends
Pomegranate, fruit and juice	Coconut water	Salmon, lox
Chicken	Breakfast cereals and granolas with nuts, dried fruit	Trail mix with nuts, dried fruits

It can feel exhausting to look over the list of foods to limit or even avoid. One of the most commonly missed foods is potatoes. Choosing other options like tortilla chips and rice cakes can make fair substitutes for potato chips. Mashed boiled cauliflower makes a decent substitute for mashed potatoes. Still, sometimes the heart wants what the heart wants, even if the kidneys aren't keen. While it is a significant amount of work, potatoes can be blanched to allow more in the diet than would otherwise be allowed and can satisfy a craving. Talk with your doctor about the amount of blanched potatoes you can serve to be sure that your loved one stays at a good level for their degree of kidney function. Remember that this process also strips out a lot of other beneficial vitamins and minerals so it is best for those who can tolerate potassium to eat fresh potatoes with no blanching and soaking.

LEACHING POTASSIUM FROM POTATOES[26]

Fresh Potatoes

Previously, patients were told to soak potatoes but combining this with boiling reduces potassium the most. The smaller the dice or slice of potato, the more potassium will be leached out. Cut the potatoes into half-inch or thinner slices or cubes less than an inch on each side. It is also important to use an enormous amount of water, at least five times the volume of potatoes. Boil for 8 minutes, drain, rinse, and add fresh water. Soak for at least two hours. To best lower the potassium, drain and add more fresh water every four hours for a total of twelve. Drain, pat dry, and use for salads, mashed potatoes, hash browns, or fries.

Canned Potatoes

---

[26] Accessed on 12/21/21
https://www.kidneycommunitykitchen.ca/dietitians-blog/lower-potassium-potatoes/

Because canned potatoes have already been boiled, they only need to be soaked. Drain and rinse the potatoes and cover with at least five times the amount of water. Soak and prepare as leeched fresh potatoes.

It is easier to choose from the lowest potassium foods rather than have to worry about the amounts of higher potassium foods. There are actually a lot of foods from which to choose. Remember that cooking and canning foods lowers potassium which is why some foods can be eaten cooked even if not appropriate when raw. Some foods might not be appropriate for all patients so it is important to be clear with your renal dietitian.

Low Potassium Foods[27][28]		
Apples, applesauce, and juice	Alfalfa sprouts	Canned apricots in juice
Cranberries, fruit and juice	Blackberries, cherries, strawberries,	Fruit cocktail

---

[27] Accessed on 11/20/21 https://www.webmd.com/a-to-z-guides/diet-and-chronic-kidney-disease

[28] Accessed on 12/21/21 https://www.kidney.org/atoz/content/potassium

	blueberries, raspberries	
Grapes, fruit and juice	Plums, fresh	Pineapples
Peaches	Pears	Nectarines
Watermelon (limited)	Cabbage, red or green	Boiled cauliflower
Asparagus	Green beans, wax beans	Celery
Cucumber	Cauliflower	Corn
Carrots, canned or cooked	Celery	Eggplant
Kale	Lettuce	Onions
Parsley	Green peas	Radishes
Peppers	Rhubarb	Water chestnut
Watercress	Rice	Garlic, fresh and jarred
Zucchini, yellow squash	White pasta, bread, cake	Goat

		cheese[29]

LOWER POTASSIUM RECIPES:

- Creamed Vegetable Soups, choose the dairy-free option
- Soupe Alexander, choose the dairy-free option
- Chicken and Dumpling Soup
- Sopa de Arroz (Mexican Rice Soup)
- Basic Fruit Gelatin
- Fruit Studded Gelatin
- Basic Aspic
- Kholodets (Studded Aspic), do not use salmon
- Fudge Pops, use the dairy-free option
- Flavored Non-Dairy Coffee Creamer
- Herb-Infused Simple Syrup
- Spiced Simple Syrup
- Simple Iced Tea by the Pitcher
- Russian Style Tea by the Pitcher
- Lemonade
- Mulling Spices for Apple Juice, Apple Cider, Wine
- Hot Toddy

---

[29] Accessed on 12/21/21
https://www.plantpoweredkidneys.com/potassium-in-cheese/

- Lower Phosphorus White Sauce Mix
- Gentle Cooked Cereal
- Rich Cooked Cereal
- Gentle Scrambled Eggs
- Rich Scrambled Eggs
- Mini Meatloaves
- Chicken Salad Spread
- Watched Pot Hard-Boiled Eggs
- Easy Oven Baked Hard-Cooked Eggs
- Berry Compote
- High-Protein Sorbet
- Whipped Coconut Cream
- Coconut Milk Fruit Sorbet
- Fruit Juice Granita (Chipped Ice)
- Homemade Vegetable Purees, avoid beets and carrots
- Oven Roasted Zucchini

PHOSPHORUS REDUCED DIET

Phosphorus plays many important roles in the body including cooperating with calcium to build strong bones and teeth. Most people eat plenty of phosphorus-rich foods and consume more than they need. Healthy kidneys excrete this excess to keep a proper balance. If the kidneys are struggling, then an excess of phosphorus in the blood can actually cause the weakening of the bones and teeth because it will leach calcium out of those bones. This free calcium can deposit in other parts of the body like in the circulatory system including the heart and blood vessels as well as the lungs and even the eyes.

One of the ways that your renal dietician might recommend reducing the intake of phosphorus is by switching to plant-based sources of protein because it is less bioavailable, this means that our bodies aren't able to absorb as much phosphorus from plant sources[30]. One of the challenges of this diet is that it also impacts protein absorption because plant-based sources are not well absorbed. If your dietician and doctor have not told you to reduce protein, be sure to be clear about your specific instructions. Kidney diets are notoriously difficult to balance. Your medical provider will be able to connect you with a dietician who specializes in kidney diets.

Phosphorus is plentiful in food and is not well removed in dialysis[31] so it might be very important to continue to restrict it. Sometimes a doctor will prescribe a medication[32] that is taken with every meal, snack, and beverage that will bind with phosphorus in the digestive tract so that it can be passed in the stool instead of being

---

[30] Acceseed on 12/21/21
https://ods.od.nih.gov/factsheets/Phosphorus-HealthProfessional/
[31] Accessed on 12/21/21
https://www.kidneyfund.org/assets/pdf/training/phosphorus-in-the-kidney-disease-diet.pdf
[32] Accesed in 12/21/21
https://consultqd.clevelandclinic.org/hyperphosphatemia-in-kidney-disease-how-to-choose-a-phosphorus-binder/

absorbed in the body. If your loved one is on a phosphorus restricted diet, you will have to carefully read all ingredient labels for added phosphorus. Naturally occurring phosphorus is actually less well absorbed than additives. Your body will actually absorb 100% of the added phosphorus in any food. Any ingredient with "phos" in its name is a form of phosphorus.

Percentage of Phosphorus Absorbed[33]	
100%	Additives in Food
80%	Naturally in dairy
60%	Naturally in meat and nuts
40%	Naturally in grains

This means that it is critical to check labels to look for additive sources of phosphorus. It can be found in places that are surprising. For instance, shrimp are often sprayed with a chemical slurry during harvesting and before freezing. Sometimes this slurry includes sodium triphosphate (also called sodium tripolyphosphate) which not only imparts a chemical taste but also forces the shrimp

---

[33] American Kindey Fund Educational Materials Accessed on 12/21/21
https://www.kidneyfund.org/assets/pdf/training/phosphorus-in-the-kidney-disease-diet.pdf

to hold more water in the tissue. It makes them heavier, rubbery, and tasteless but can also be dangerous for those on kidney diets[34]. Tripolyphosphate is often used as a "plumper" on peeled shrimp, so it is often better to buy shrimp with peels. The added benefit is that you can later use the peels for stock.

Another surprising source of phosphorus is non-dairy whipped topping which uses sodium polyphosphate as a preservative[35]. A better option is homemade whipped dairy cream which has no added phosphorus. The same is true for other milk substitutes like almond milk and non-dairy coffee creamer, both of which are easy to make from scratch and take little effort. There are recipes for whipped cream in the Dessert section of this book and coffee creamer in the Beverages section. If looking for a good alternative to milk, look for coconut milk-based substitutes and check for "phos" in the ingredients list. Many coconut-based products are good options but it depends on the additives. You also make your own with canned coconut milk. Combine one full can with two cans of water and mix well and use it as replacement milk. If you are used to using packaged sauce mixes that are notoriously high in added

---

[34] Accessed on 12/21/21
https://www.nytimes.com/2019/10/15/dining/shrimp-additives.html
[35] Accessed on 12/21/21 https://www.heb.com/product-detail/kraft-cool-whip-extra-creamy-whipped-topping/2235972

phosphorus, in the Entree section there is a handy homemade mix version.

Foods High in Added Phosphorus	
Processed meats, sausages	Some shrimp, scallops, other seafood
Instant puddings	Instant sauce mixes
Spreadable cheeses	Boxed macaroni and cheese
Colas, dark soda (clear and light-colored sodas like ginger ale and lemon-lime are safe)	Some bottled iced teas (choose homemade)
Coffee creamer, milk substitutes	Pancake, biscuit, breading mixes
Flavored gelatin	Canned tuna
Fast food	Purchased bread, rolls, buns, tortillas
Calcium based heartburn tablets	Breakfast cereal

Phosphorus is broadly used as a food preservative so more processed foods will be more likely to have more phosphorus. It is also a critical ingredient in baking powder, in both aluminum[36] and non-aluminum varieties[37], making it important to be careful about purchased baked goods. Prepared gelatin mixes contain added phosphorus, so homemade versions are a better solution and are surprisingly easy to make. They are hardly more effort. Studies show that when phosphate-added foods are included in the diet versus diets that only include naturally occurring phosphorus, it can contribute more than 1000mg a day of phosphorus to the diet[38]. Be sure to check even if you don't expect phosphorus additives.

Examples of Added Phosphorus		
Phosphoric acid	Sodium polyphosphate	Pyro-phosphate
Sodium tripoly-phosphate	Polyphosphate	Sodium phosphate
Tricalcium phosphate	Hexameta-phosphate	Trisodium phosphate

---

[36] Accessed on 12/21/21
https://cdn.thomasnet.com/ccp/10020857/79307.pdf
[37] Accessed on 12/21/21 https://www.heb.com/product-detail/rumford-aluminum-free-baking-powder/132529
[38] Accessed on https://www.sciencedirect.com/topics/medicine-and-dentistry/food-preservative

Dicalcium phosphate	Aluminum phosphate	Tetrasodium-phosphate
Monocalcium phosphate	Ferric phosphate	Sodium aluminum phosphate

LOWER PHOSPHORUS RECIPES:

- Creamed Vegetable Soups
- Soupe Alexander
- Chicken and Dumpling Soup
- Beef and Barley Soup, omit beef
- Creamy Mushroom Soup
- Sopa de Arroz (Mexican Rice Soup)
- Basic Fruit Gelatin
- Fruit Studded Gelatin
- Fudge Pops, choose non-dairy option
- Flavored Non-Dairy Coffee Creamer
- Herb-Infused Simple Syrup
- Spiced Simple Syrup
- Simple Iced Tea by the Pitcher
- Russian Style Tea by the Pitcher
- Lemonade
- Mexican Style Hot Chocolate
- Mulling Spices for Apple Juice, Apple Cider, Wine
- Hot Toddy
- Lower Phosphorus White Sauce Mix
- Gentle Cooked Cereal
- Rich Cooked Cereal
- Gentle Scrambled Eggs

- Easy Macaroni and Cheese, still high in dairy so limit consumption
- Mini Meatloaves
- Chicken Salad Spread
- Watched Pot Hard-Boiled Eggs
- Easy Oven Baked Hard-Cooked Eggs
- Berry Compote
- Whipped Coconut Cream
- Coconut Milk Fruit Sorbet
- Fruit Juice Granita (Chipped Ice)
- Homemade Vegetable Purees
- Maple Cinnamon Carrots
- Buttered Spiced Beets
- Oven Roasted Zucchini

LOW PROTEIN DIET

Protein is essential for good health. It allows your body to maintain and repair all the systems of your body. If your kidneys are healthy, they can process the waste products of breaking down and using protein but this is not true for people with chronic kidney disease. To avoid strain on weakened kidneys, some patients are asked to reduce their protein intake. Exactly what the limit is for protein depends on the stage of kidney disease and whether or not the patient is receiving dialysis. Some renal dieticians will counsel you to include more plant-based protein in your loved one's diet to accommodate their needs for protein but stay under the amount animal sources provide.

Another way to reduce the protein that we eat is to serve smaller portions and combine them with other low-protein foods like fruits and vegetables. Filling out salad and sandwiches and soups with lots of vegetables are good ways of stretching less protein to help it feel more satisfying. Using more pasta, rice, or other grains in soups, stir-fries, and casseroles can only make a meal look and feel more filling when the protein is limited. Use non-dairy, low protein alternatives for milk or cream in rice and soups to cut back without feeling deprived. Stronger-tasting cheeses like blue cheese and parmesan can allow you to use a lot less without sacrificing flavor.

Animal protein foods include meats like beef and pork and poultry like chicken and turkey as well as fish and seafood. Eggs and dairy are also high-quality sources of animal protein. Good plant-based sources include beans and nuts and grains. A mix of animal and plant-based proteins will yield good results. Talk to your medical provider about the exact amounts allowed.

LOWER PROTEIN RECIPES:

- Creamed Vegetable Soups, perhaps dairy-free
- Soupe Alexander, perhaps dairy-free
- Beef and Barley Soup, omit beef

- Creamy Mushroom Soup, perhaps dairy-free
- Sopa de Arroz (Mexican Rice Soup)
- Basic Fruit Gelatin
- Basic Creamy Gelatin
- Fruit Studded Gelatin
- Fudge Pops, perhaps dairy-free option
- Flavored Non-Dairy Coffee Creamer
- Herb-Infused Simple Syrup
- Spiced Simple Syrup
- Simple Iced Tea by the Pitcher
- Russian Style Tea by the Pitcher
- Lemonade
- Mulling Spices for Apple Juice, Apple Cider, Wine
- Hot Toddy
- Lower Phosphorus White Sauce Mix
- Gentle Cooked Cereal
- Berry Compote
- Whipped Cream
- Whipped Coconut Cream
- Coconut Milk Fruit Sorbet
- Fruit Juice Granita (Chipped Ice)
- Homemade Vegetable Purees
- Maple Cinnamon Carrots
- Buttered Spiced Beets
- Creamed Spinach
- Oven Roasted Zucchini

CHAPTER TWO: APPEALING MEALS

"When you sit down to eat, pray. When you eat bread, do so thanking Him for being so generous to you. If you drink wine, be mindful of Him who has given it to you for your pleasure and as a relief in sickness." -St Basil the Great

ONE OF THE CHALLENGES OF CARING for a loved one at home is simply getting them to eat. We can know what the diet requires, we can have a stack of recipes at hand, we can have help in the kitchen, we can have meals brought to the house but none of it will matter if we cannot convince someone to eat. During periods of extreme physical stress caused by illness or injury, we tend to turn inwards with just the effort of healing. The interest in food and the appetite can be all but absent. If there are physical limitations that make the process of eating or digesting more difficult, these challenges can cause people to decide that food might not be worth the effort. Keeping portions small can prevent tiring the patient. Increasing the number of meals per day is a better way of increasing the amount of food eaten over the course of a day rather than just serving larger portions.

It might be difficult for your loved one to sit up and be stable enough to both eat and swallow. Make sure they are well supported on both sides and from behind. Bed trays are easy to find and can allow patients to sit in bed while they eat. Sometimes it can be exhausting to move to a new place to eat and that energy might be better spent simply eating. If your loved one needs more support for their arms while eating, try rolling a towel and laying it close to their body. This can support their arm while eating which can make the process less tiring.

Bibs can serve an important role in keeping the clothes and bed clean but they can also feel demeaning, childlike. Try using an attractive tea towel that can be laid over the chest or tucked in at the neck. If your loved one will be recovering for a long time, napkin clips can be found online that will let you turn any piece of fabric into a more appropriate bib. For more or less permanent conditions, you can turn second-hand men's shirts into attractive bibs. Using either a button-up shirt with either short or long sleeves, cut the back portion out of the shirt leaving the side seam attached to the front of the shirt to prevent unraveling. Cut up both sides, leaving the sleeves for now, to the yoke, and then cut along the bottom of the yoke or the panel behind the shoulders. Leave the seam attached to the yoke to prevent unraveling. Cut the sleeves off but leave the seam attached to the remainder of the shirt, again, to prevent unraveling. This leaves a shirt front with buttons and a collar which allows it to look and feel more like normal clothing. Women's shirts can be used if they don't have shaping at the waist or bust darts which makes them not lay flat.

It is important to remember that there is a certain loss of dignity that can be humbling. Not being able to eat neatly so that a bib is necessary can make someone feel more vulnerable. To be fed with a syringe to not be able to eat whole pieces of food will take a further emotional toll. When we are caring for someone with serious limitations, we have to be sensitive to these feelings. Be patient during meal times, nutrition is critically important to their recovery, and allow them the time necessary to eat. This might impact other things that need your attention but try to remember that food is medicine and that this time is well spent.

When you, the caregiver, need an opportunity for respite or a chance to vent, vent outward and not towards the person that you are caring for. This is certainly difficult for you to manage and they are most definitely aware of that. Adding the weight of your concerns to their own can be unbearable. Be sensitive to their needs and seek professional emotional support before it becomes a crisis. Convalescents can have strong emotions and sometimes they are afraid to share them. When I was critically ill, I would cry alone in the bathroom and then put on a brave face for my family when I came out. I should have been more honest about my needs and fears and I should not have let them fester.

This need to be honest about the need for professional help extends to you, as well. The stress of caring for an ill family member can cause an enormous amount of trauma and your inner circle might forget that you have needs. Find a good supportive friend or even an organized group to join, in person or online, to give you a safe space to process your own feelings about this time. Remember that your loved one is not the illness or injury but still the same person that they always were. Be cheerful and bright and talk to them to keep their interaction up without talking down to them. Don't belittle them further by using childish language even if you must speak slower or more loudly.

Eating can feel lonely and isolating. Staying with them, or asking someone else to stay with them, can make it a more enjoyable experience. Sometimes patients need a distraction, especially for the longer periods needed for feeding with a syringe. Try playing music or an audiobook or even watching a film. Feeding can feel like a time-consuming task that deprives both you and your loved one of time to do other tasks so try to bring a sense of leisure activities into the meal so that they are more pleasant. Just don't be so consumed by the plot that you forget to eat!

Sometimes the refusal to eat can be a way to exert some measure of control over their lives. The less they are able to do for themselves, the less control they have over their lives, the weaker they feel. Deciding to not eat might feel like the only aspect of their lives that they have control over. It can help to offer them some choices. It might be a choice of two items to eat or the order in which to eat them. Choosing a book or movie or music to listen to can give them more power and some level of independence back.

Keep the environment attractive. This might sound silly but it really isn't. When we go out to dinner, we want a good environment because it contributes to the overall dining experience. When the diet is limited and perhaps your loved one isn't able to feed themselves, anything that makes the meal more pleasant will encourage eating. Set out candles, electric ones are a great option for people on oxygen, and use a colorful placemat. Choose pretty dishes and maybe even a little centerpiece. When I was critically ill, one of my sons made a little Lego version of me and brought it to me while I was eating in bed. I cannot tell you how much good it did for me but it was also good for him. Helping set trays can be a way for a child to interact with and contribute to the care of a loved one. Small sculptures, drawings, and other arts and crafts can make them feel a part of the family effort and can be a bright spot in the day of a recovering patient.

If your loved one is able to feed themselves but finds it to be challenging, remember that the dishes and cutlery you choose can make this harder. When hands are weak and unsteady, lighter and smaller cups with sturdy handles are easier to use. Glass dishes are pretty but if they are heavy or there is a concern about breakage, it can make meal times more stressful. Look for attractive but lightweight and unbreakable dishes and glassware. If spilling is a concern, look for commuter mugs with openings to drink from rather than spouts and straws. There are many, many conditions that make straws inappropriate. Look in the baby section of the store for cutlery designed for toddlers. These have thicker handles and a more ergonomic shape which can make it easier to self-feed. Dishes should be light enough for your loved one to manipulate without strain. Remember that recovery is already a great deal of effort, they might not have much energy or strength to spare. If your loved one needs additional support learning how to eat and drink again, talk to your healthcare provider about a referral to an occupational therapist. These professionals are unsung heroes in convalescence and can help both the patient and the caregiver find solutions.

Dehydration is a real concern for convalescents and often causes worry but don't offer too much to drink at meals. It might cause your loved one to fill up their stomach with low nutrition drinks and they won't get the calories that they need. Unless they are on a fluid-restricted diet, encourage lots of drinking between meals rather than with the meal itself. If caring for someone who is reticent, adding fruit slices and herbs to the water can make it taste more appealing. Cucumber, apple, citrus (if appropriate), basil, and mint (if appropriate) can make water a little more pleasant to drink. Don't forget to keep your own cup full to ensure that you are also fully hydrated to keep up your health. See the beverages section for more ideas.

Kidney patients might need to have a steady supply of sugar-free candies instead as a way of soothing thirst. It is especially important to be sure to carry these around when out and about. Be considerate of their inability to drink and perhaps try to keep your own full cup in another room. Drink often but not in front of someone who is unable to drink.

Some patients will need to be fed through a tube inserted in the nose or through the abdominal wall. It is possible to feed prepared formula using a syringe in this way using a port or through a bag on a pump. Many of the liquid and puree recipes in this book will be appropriate for this sort of feeding. Talk to your medical provider about adding homemade foods to your loved one's diet. It can give a caregiver some solace to be able to make homemade food for someone they love so much. Children especially miss treats like ice cream and even if they cannot enjoy the pleasure of eating them, they can receive a lot of emotional comfort being fed treats through their ports. The pleasures of eating go both ways, it is a comfort and joy to both the cook and the patient.

Some patients who are very sick and not able to feed themselves well but who don't need this kind of support can be better fed using oral syringes. Foods from the Full Liquid Diet section can be fed in this way. It can be slow and laborious but can provide significant nutrition. Slowly press the plunger and give pauses between "bites" to allow your loved one to swallow. It might help to ask them to open their mouth so that there is no encouragement to suck on the syringe which might be inappropriate and even damaging. The syringe in this case is more like a closed spoon, you are placing small amounts in the mouth and not injecting it.

If your loved one cannot have solid food, this is often distressing for them. You can mold food to make it look more like the original. You can buy silicone molds online that will allow you to shape food like chicken drumsticks, pork chops, a pile of green peas, or chicken breasts. These are expensive and time-consuming to use but can really support the well-being of someone who misses standard fare. Candy molds and silicone ice cube trays are often less expensive and can make fun shapes that aren't natural but can be entertaining. Using molded foods as a treat can keep it from being overwhelming for you to prepare but allow you to give your loved one something special that is still allowed on their diet. Check the recipe section for molded foods.

Another way of keeping meals complex and interesting is to mix serving temperatures. When the ingredients list is restricted, mixing frozen, chilled, room temperature, and hot foods gives different ways to experience flavors. It is also another way you can give your loved one a chance to make decisions. Giving more options for how to eat food might help them feel more in control of their eating and can reduce refusals. This is another way in which silicone food molds can be helpful. Puddings, custards, and fruit whips can be frozen in molds to create fun-shaped treats. Fruit whips are higher in protein than pudding and can be another way of increasing overall protein in the diet. They are also helpful for getting children to eat.

The same thing is true for texture. Using as many textures as possible allows mouthfeel to be a bigger part of the experience and makes a diet feel more varied when it is already limited. It is also another opportunity for the convalescent to exercise dietary control in a safe and healthy way. Offering more variety encourages them in a personal decision to eat so they are less likely to choose to not eat.

Restricted diets feel restricted. There is often the sense that something is missing and this can take a toll on patients who need to keep their spirits up to keep their strength up. Whenever possible, add new twists to food that maintain their dietary restrictions but allow you to present food in another way. Try toasting or warming bread and rolls to avoid always serving cold foods. You can reheat a roll or a few pieces of bread in the microwave, just dampen a paper towel to cover them to prevent moisture loss. You can achieve the same thing by wrapping them in aluminum foil and warming them in a 350F oven or a toaster oven for 10-15 minutes. If you have an air fryer, set it to 325F and heat it for 3-4 minutes.

Broiling or air frying food can also give an interesting texture when much of the food is boiled or baked and often mashed so long as the patient is not on a mechanically soft diet. Warm allowed canned fruit in the syrup with a cinnamon stick for a different twist when fruit cocktail is feeling old. Toasting white rice in a dry pan before adding the cooking liquid adds a rich, nutty flavor without adding nuts or other difficult-to-digest ingredients. To meet the needs of the GI soft diet and to avoid heartburn cook soups, use toothpicks to spear large pieces of onion and garlic, and cook with the rest of the ingredients. Remove the garlic and onion before serving. This way you can add flavor without going off the diet.

One of the greatest dangers in severe illness and injury is weight loss and the risk of muscle wasting. Encourage more consumption of higher calorie and protein-rich foods. If your loved one has asked for a second cookie, ask them if they would also like a cube of cheese or a little cottage cheese with it. Small pieces of meat like cubed ham or Vienna sausages can be a way of introducing quick, easy-to-serve protein though they are very high in sodium. Additionally, Vienna sausages often contain nutmeg and garlic, both of which contribute to heartburn and aren't appropriate for a GI Soft diet but can be an occasional snack for most people. Hard-boiled eggs, whole or sliced, or even cubed, are a great way to introduce calories and protein. See the Entrees section for the standard method of boiling eggs but also an incredibly easy baked method. A few pieces of shredded rotisserie chicken are easy to serve and easy to eat for most patients. Cold or warm, a small meatball is another way to add just a bit more protein. The Entree section also has a meatball recipe that uses heavy cream for an additional calorie boost. Anytime you can add protein to a meal or a snack unless your loved one is on a protein-restricted diet, you should do it.

When patients are not eating well, it is tempting to resort to treats and sweets as a means of gaining compliance. This is a short-term gain that actually can cause more problems since these foods tend to be less nutritious and of little protein. Because protein is critical for tissue repair, it is critical in the diet throughout the healing process. Unless your loved one is on a protein-reduced diet because of advanced kidney disease, prioritize protein. Make a source of protein a central part of every meal and find ways of incorporating more. For instance, when making pureed foods, use bone broth or instant meal replacer as the liquid to boost the protein further. Whey protein powder, long a darling of weightlifters, often comes in a variety of flavors and can make a flavorful addition to coffee (if allowed), or added to fruit whips, and milkshakes.

Another good protein source when pureeing foods is cottage cheese or Greek-style yogurt, full-fat if calories are needed and fat-free for GI Soft diets. A half a cup of cottage cheese has more than 8g of protein[39]. Greek yogurt is strained to remove extra whey which makes it more concentrated and a similar portion has, almost 10g[40]. Pudding is often offered as a protein source in hospitals, probably because it is sweet and more likely to be eaten, but it is actually a poor source. A pudding cup, which is usually just over half a cup, only has a single gram of protein[41]! This is insufficient for helping patients who need good protein sources in order to build back muscle mass and heal injured tissues. The Fruits and Desserts and the Gelatins sections both include

[39] Accessed 12/23/21 https://fdc.nal.usda.gov/fdc-app.html#/food-details/560705/nutrients
[40] Acessed on 12/23/21 https://fdc.nal.usda.gov/fdc-app.html#/food-details/170903/nutrients
[41] Accessed on 12/23/21 https://fdc.nal.usda.gov/fdc-app.html#/food-details/657118/nutrients

better options for treats than store-bought pudding cups and ice cream.

When you offer snacks, try to avoid sweets and simple carbohydrates and look for protein-based foods. Instead of offering plain sliced and peeled apples, spread a layer of peanut butter over each slice. Chicken, tuna, and egg salad make great sandwich spreads but can also be served with crackers or allowed vegetables like baby carrots, snap peas, or slices of bell pepper. Cheese sticks are easy to keep on hand and require no prep and each one has almost 7g of protein[42]. For an additional protein boost, you can wrap a slice of lunchmeat around the cheese but remember that these tend to be very high in sodium and phosphorus and not good choices for those on renal diets.

TIPS FOR MAKING CONVALESCENT MEALS MORE APPEALING

1. Place them in a supported and comfortable position
2. Smaller, more frequent meals are better for overall nutrition.
3. Be patient at mealtimes, invest in this part of care.
4. Provide cheerful and bright distractions like music, audiobooks, or movies.

---

[42] Accessed on 12/24/21 https://fdc.nal.usda.gov/fdc-app.html#/food-details/170847/nutrients

5. Make the atmosphere attractive and appealing with candles and centerpieces.
6. Look for cups light enough to be held and with sturdy handles. Remember, straws are not always appropriate.
7. Limit beverages at meals to avoid and encourage drinking between meals.
8. Easy to use cutlery, think about baby and toddler ones for weak handholds and lightweight plastic ones made to look like real versions.
9. Using a syringe to feed someone is more like spoon-feeding.
10. Using molds to make pureed food look more like the original
11. Serve foods at a variety of temperatures and a mix of textures.
12. Prioritize protein.

CHAPTER THREE: BROTH AND STOCK

BONE BROTH IS THE MODERN FOOD movement darling but, ironically, it is not actually broth but stock. Culinarily speaking, the nutritious and flavorful liquid we make by the long-simmering of bones is called stock. Broth is a meat-based liquid made by simmering meat and sometimes vegetables for a short period of time. It is probably not worth the confusion or argument to keep the distinction here so I will just use the term bone broth to indicate the kind of stock that I am talking about.

Bone broth is a nearly universal food for those who are convalescing and really forms the foundation for healing foods. If there are any universal foods that virtually everyone can consume, broth surely is one. While it is true that those on liquid restricted diets cannot have significant amounts but, if it is used to replace the water in the preparation of foods like rice, it can provide much-needed nutrition without increasing fluid intake.

Many times, hospitals will offer broth to patients on full liquid diets or those with physical challenges to eating. The problem is that what comes on the tray is not actually broth but rather a packet of powdered broth mix and a plastic mug of hot water covered with a plastic lid, a little vent letting out the steam. This is not broth; it is a kind of placeholder for the broth that we used to serve convalescents when they recovered in those sickrooms in the home. I don't know if modern American hospitals ever served real broth but I do know that they no longer do. While I am grateful for the medical care that hospitals provide, dietary support is not one of the things that they excel at.

When I was repeatedly hospitalized after Sophia's birth, I had many, many trays with the plastic mug and a green packet of broth powder. The brand that I was given then currently has this list of ingredients listed on its website:

*"...with Other Natural Flavors Ingredients: Salt, Flavor (Hydrolyzed Corn Protein, Salt), Sugar, contains 2% or less of Chicken Fat, Disodium Inosinate and Disodium Guanylate, **Dehydrated Cooked Chicken** (Contains Natural Flavor), Silicon Dioxide (Anticaking Agent), Turmeric, Dehydrated Parsley, Onion Powder, Spice, Garlic Powder"*[43] *(emphasis mine)*

On ingredient lists, the items are listed by the percentage of the total weight that it represents. The higher on an ingredient list a component is

---

[43] Herb-Ox Chicken Flavored Boullion Granules ingredients accessed 10/09/21 https://hormel.com/Brands/HORMEL-Herb-Ox/Herbox-Packets/Granulated-Chicken-Bouillon-Packets

found, it means that makes up a greater percentage of the product by weight, that there is just more of it there[44]. When we analyze this label, we see that there is more salt in this powdered mix than there is chicken. When I make either broth or stock, I would never add more salt than actual meat. It is also important to note that this mix contains no measurable amount of nutrition except for an enormous amount of sodium, nearly half the day's recommended allowance (see the comparison chart that follows). This is hardly surprising given the vast number of ingredients that are sodium-based.

This company also makes a sodium free version which avoids the excessive amount of salt by replacing this flavor enhancer with potassium chloride. This is important to note because some kidney patients who are on sodium reducing diets also need to avoid potassium making this product not safe for them to eat. While it is less salty, it is no more nutritious and still manages to contain no chicken meat, only chicken fat.

"...with Other Natural Flavors Ingredients: Sugar, Potassium Chloride, Onion Powder, Maltodextrin, Monoammonium Glutamate, Gelatin, Dextrose, **Chicken Fat***, Contains 2% or less of Silicon Dioxide (Anticaking Agent), Dehydrated Parsley, Natural*

---

[44] https://www.hsph.harvard.edu/nutritionsource/food-label-guide/ accessed 10/9/21

Flavoring, Disodium Inosinate and Disodium Guanylate*, Polysorbate 80, Turmeric Extractive, Propylene Glycol. *Adds a dietarily insignificant amount of sodium."[45] *(emphasis mine)*

This is not the sort of food to form a comforting and healing foundation for me to rebuild my health but I, fortunately, had people caring for me. When I was hospitalized, my best friend made me broth and brought it in large thermoses every time she visited. One visit followed surgery and the protocol required that I be able to eat and drink a certain amount and the requisite broth packets arrived but I did not drink them. Instead, I sipped the nutritious homemade broth she made.

Korrine York, my medical consultant for this book, has spent years working with critically ill children as a certified pediatric nurse working in a major urban hospital. She feels very strongly about real bone broth (stock) having the occasion to compare two patients she cared for at the same time. It is important to note that I do not know their diagnoses or names or ages or even genders. All I know is that they were in similar condition and one drank the green packets and the other drank broth made by the mother. The child who was fed the homemade broth recovered more

---

[45] Herb-Ox Chicken Flavored Boullion Granules, Sodium Free, from Hormel Foods ingredients accessed 10/9/21
https://www.hormel.com/Brands/HORMEL-Herb-Ox/Herbox-Packets/sodium-free-chicken

quickly and made substantial improvements to the degree that it changed her perspectives on how she wanted to feed her family. She wanted to start making bone broth from scratch despite not having emphasized it in her diet before.

Some of us have grown up with parents and grandparents who saved bones for stock. If so, you might think that broth made from bones is frugal and perhaps not as nutritious as that made with the meat itself. This is far from the truth. Broth made with meat is actually significantly less nutritious because the meat will actually become very tough if cooked for long lengths of time so it is usually cooked only for a very short period. It also means that it is less flavorful which makes it less palatable and it is thinner because it does not have the collagen that provides body to bone broth. It also contains half the calories which is significant if a patient is relying on broth as an important source of nutrition during recovery. My husband compares the broth made with meat to a sort of tea, it is not flavorless or nutritionless but it lacks the depth of that made with bones. Broth made with the bones requires long cooking, several hours, and the time allows minerals and collagen to be extracted. The resulting broth is very fragrant and thick and tastes rich and satisfying in addition to being highly nourishing. You can easily tell the difference between these foods after refrigeration, bone broth will gel and meat-based broth will still be thin and liquidy. Bone broth is not just a money-saving utility but a health-improving food that can make a significant difference for your loved one as they convalesce.

There is clinical evidence for the healing benefits of bone broth. A 2017 study of the recovery strategies of competitive athletes found that collagen and gelatin, like that found in bone broth, actually improved the depth of knee cartilage and decreased knee pain[46]. Another 2017 study shows how glutamine, an amino acid that can be found in bone-based broths, might improve gut health by regulating intestinal permeability. The data is very much in the preliminary stage but shows promise and will hopefully be better studied in the future[47].

We know that bone broth feels comforting to sip and it certainly soothing but it might also promote good sleep. Glycine is another amino acid found in bone broth and it acts as a neurotransmitter in the brain. A 2015 study found that rats given oral doses of glycine promoted sleep when they experienced stress that disrupted it, things like being transferred into new, clean

---

[46] Selected In-Season Nutritional Strategies to Enhance Recovery for Team Sport Athletes: A Practical Overview Sports Med. 2017; 47(11): 2201–2218.
https://www.ncbi.nlm.nih.gov/pmc/articles/PMC5633631/ accessed 10/9/21
[47] Glutamine and the Regulation of Intestinal Permability
https://pubmed.ncbi.nlm.nih.gov/27749689/ accessed on 10/9/21

cages.

While I cannot guarantee that your loved one will sleep better or have better health of the knees or gut, I can assure you that they will be better nourished by bone broth than powdered packets. Below you will find an analysis of regular, low sodium, chicken meat, and chicken bone-based broths. When we compare the nutritional value of real bone broth compared to the powdered, there is no question about what we should choose.

COMPARISONS BETWEEN INSTANT, MEAT-BASED, AND BONE-BASED BROTH

	One Packet Prepared with Water		One Cup of Prepared Broth[48]	
Nutrition Facts	Instant Broth Regular[49]	Instant Broth	Meat Based Broth	Bone Based (Stock) Broth

---

[48] Nutrition information for both meat-based broth and bone-based stock accessed on 10/9/21
https://www.medicalnewstoday.com/articles/stock-vs-broth#how-to-use-them

[49]Herb-Ox Chicken Flavored Sodium Free Boullion Granules from Hormel Foods nutrition facts accessed on 10/9/21
https://hormel.com/Brands/HORMEL-Herb-Ox/Herbox-Packets/Granulated-Chicken-Bouillon-Packets
https://www.medicalnewstoday.com/articles/stock-vs-broth#how-to-use-them

		Sodium Free[50]		
Calories	5	10	38	86
Carbohydrates	1g	2g	2.9g	8.5g
Fat	0g	0g	1.4g	2.9g
Protein	0g	0g	4.8g	6g
Potassium (% of recommended daily allowance or RDA)	Not listed but contains Potassium Chloride	-	6%	7%
Riboflavin (% RDA)	-	-	4%	12%
B6 (% RDA)	-	-	1%	7%
Phosphorus (% RDA)	-	-	7%	6%
Niacin (% RDA)	0	0	16%	19%
Thiamine (% RDA)	-	-	0%	6%

---

[50] Herb-Ox Chicken Flavored Bouillon Granules from Hormel Foods nutrition facts accessed on 10/9/21
https://www.hormel.com/Brands/HORMEL-Herb-Ox/Herbox-Packets/sodium-free-chicken

Folate (% RDA)	-	-	0%	3%
Selenium (% RDA)	-	-	0%	8%
Sodium	1,100 mg	0	Sodium Varies	Sodium Varies

It is also important to state again that the salt in the sodium-free broth is made using a significant amount of potassium chloride, more than the chicken fat added to flavor it. Potassium chloride is an electrolyte that replaces the salt flavor in sodium-reduced foods.

MAKING BONE BROTH

Looking up recipes on the internet is only occasionally helpful, but more commonly frustrating, and looking up making broth is no exception. One of the challenges facing caregivers is that their time is at a premium and lengthy and complicated recipes only serve to sap their resources of strength and time. Bone broth was made successfully by illiterate people living on subsistence farms with more children and fewer resources than modern people. It does not need to be an expensive or exhausting proposition, there is no need to make it harder than it needs to be. In its most basic form, it is bones and water. That is all it takes. You do need, of course, a vessel, and you could add some adjuncts, but the basic recipe is the same:

Bones + Water + Time = Bone Broth

If you know someone caring for a loved one and they are pressed for time, it can be an extraordinary thing to prepare a batch of bone broth for them. This liberates them and allows them to spend their time doing other tasks or perhaps even rest. Along these same lines, if you are a caregiver or are convalescing yourself, do not be afraid to ask someone to make broth for you when they offer help.

In the absence of help and resources, it is not only possible to buy bone broth at the store but a solid nutritional choice. When looking for store-bought versions, look for something that contains at least six grams of protein per cup and is labeled as reduced sodium. In the United States, in order to use the phrase "reduced sodium", the version must have **25%** less sodium than a competing equivalent product[51]. Sodium is often used as a flavor enhancer when there really isn't a lot of other flavor present and is sometimes a sign of poor-quality broth. The sodium really should be under 400mg on the upper end and if you can

---

[51] Code of Federal Regulations accessed on 11/17/21
https://www.accessdata.fda.gov/scripts/cdrh/cfdocs/cfcfr/CFR Search.cfm?fr=101.61

find unsalted, it is even better. It is not hard to add a dash or two of salt to the broth and then you are in control of what you serve your loved one.

BONES

You can use any bones that you have, even shellfish shells. If you keep a resealable plastic bag in the freezer, you can add bones from cooking and accumulate them until you have enough to make broth. The most flavorful broths have a variety of bones such as beef and chicken and pork so don't be concerned about keeping them separate. Use whatever bones are left over from other meals, the carcass from a roast chicken or turkey or bones from steak or chops, just make sure to store them in the freezer to keep them fresh. If you are making chicken or turkey and the neck is included, remember to place this in your freezer with other bones. One of the common meals that we rely on in times of strain and pressure is the store-bought rotisserie chicken. I know that when we have received meals, these were a common choice for people, especially since the size of my family intimidated people who weren't sure how to cook for us. I also know that I have bought them myself or for others when time was short but the need was great. These bones can be a ready source for a secondary meal when used to make broth and it is more than a frugal practice, it is actually very nourishing.

In some supermarkets, you can find bones for stock and this is another great source but working from these bones is admittedly a lot more work. If you are working from fresh beef or veal bones (not those from shellfish or fish), sometimes the resulting broth is aggressive tasting. If you have ever had a homemade broth made from fresh bones, particularly beef, that you thought was too musky, it probably was not properly prepared. It is one of the reasons that people tend to have a negative view of beef broth and it takes a couple of extra steps to prevent this. Rinse the bones off before putting them in a large pot (like gallon-sized) filled with fresh water. Place on the stove and bring to a rolling boil and then turn off the heat, cover, and walk away. Twenty minutes later, you can drain and then toss these bones on a deep roasting pan. Roast these in a 450F oven until dark and fragrant, at least twenty minutes. The bones should darken and not be burned but be very nearly. Dump these bones in your slow cooker or electric pressure cooker. Do not forget to add very hot water to the pan to loosen the fond (the flavorful bits left in the pan) and add this to your vessel. Your resulting broth won't have any gamey or musky taste. It is important to note that pork bones seldom have this problem and fresh poultry bones never do so if you want to avoid these steps, choose these bones or use only those from previously cooked bones.

In Orthodox Christian homes, we often rely on shellfish for protein during long fasts. I keep a bag for those shells as well and while it takes longer to amass enough for a pot of stock, those little shrimp tales make for a lovely soup later. If you are so fortunate to have other kinds of shellfish such as clams, mussels, crab, or lobster, all of these can be combined to make a delicious stock. Stock made from shellfish is the base of bisque and what makes it different from other soups. You can also make stock using fish bones and heads, oftentimes fish counters will give you those for free if you are fortunate to live in an area with fishing. If you know someone who fishes, this can be a great source. Ask this person to save the scraps after they bone their fish.

If you fast religiously, like we Orthodox Christians do, remember that the fast was never intended to harm your health or weaken your body. In order to rebuild health, it is necessary to eat the proper foods, and this can be a more important ascetic practice than fasting from animal-based foods. We are close with a particular monk at one of the largest American monasteries. Recently, this monk experienced significant health problems during a fast. His physician diagnosed him with a severe protein deficiency. The abbot gave him the obedience of eating fish daily which was a humbling experience for this young monk. I contacted donors to the monastic community and told them of his need for shelf stable packets of ready to eat fish that he could add to all of his meals. He was obedient and his health rapidly improved. He more quickly returned to his regular ascetic practices and dedicated work schedule because he fed his body as it needed. Your loved one is fasting from much at this time, even if not fasting from food in the same way. Don't add to the heavy burden of healing by adding extra obligations. Feed your loved one as they need to be fed.

WATER

It takes a substantial amount of water to cook your bone broth. One of the mistakes that people make is using an insufficient amount of it. When rinsing fresh beef or veal bones, rinse very well under cool, running water before adding to a very large kettle or pot. Fill the pot with bones without forcing more into the pot. It should be ¾ of the way filled. Cover with fresh, cool water before boiling. Do use cold water and allow it to slowly come to a boil rather than forcing it by starting with hot water. The goal here is to blanch or clean the bones and not just mechanically separate the meat and bones through instant and vigorous boiling. After you have boiled and soaked for twenty minutes, drain and discard the cooking water before roasting. There is much more extensive information on this process in the vessel section but suffice it to say that lots of fresh, cool water is a critical component.

When preparing to make broth, after the preparation steps for fresh bones, if necessary, be sure again to use lots of cool water to fill the vessel for cooking. It is better to use a little hot water to loosen the fond in the roasting pan but this amount of hot water won't be a problem. Fill your vessel with plenty of cool, fresh water and cover the bones completely but do not use more than that. There is a happy medium and you do not want to dilute your broth but you do want to use enough water to act on the bones. Avoid the temptation to crowd the pot and force more bones into a pot than would fit if just set down inside. You should allow water to circulate but do use enough bones to fill it. Because the water needs to circulate in the pot in order to extract the most nutrition out of the bones, it is important to leave room for this.

VESSEL

It can be made on the stovetop, but that makes for a steamy kitchen. You will lose water through evaporation when cooking on the stove, so it does need more tending. In the old days, the pot was pushed to the back of the stove to use the radiant heat of the cooking fuel, but in these modern days, we would need to leave a burner on. I don't recommend this method because it is not safe to leave a burner running for the length of time it takes to make a proper broth, and when making shorter cooking broths, such as fish, the odor can be so off-putting as to dissuade people from making it.

It is not only easier but better to use a slow cooker or an electric pressure cooker. These appliances are a better resource because they can really be used to extract the full potential of the minerals and nutrients of your bones, they are safer to operate for longer periods, and they can be relocated while they are running to prevent cooking odors. If using the stovetop, try to use a stockpot. These are tall and narrow and this is to allow you to use larger, longer bones but also this shape allows them to cook without losing too much liquid to evaporation. A good stock pot will hold one if not two gallons of liquid but do not prepare more broth than you have the willingness and the means to store properly. Freshly made bone broth should only be kept in the fridge for about five days.

If you are making shellfish or fish broth, you could cook this on the stovetop because these cook for a shorter period but it is important to note that this will make your house smell fishy. Fish broth will cook in only 20 minutes on the stove but you should cook shellfish for 40-45 minutes. If you are sensitive to the smell of cooking fish, it is better to cook this in a slow cooker or instant pot and consider moving this to a covered porch or patio. Because those slow cookers take longer to arrive at their cooking temperature, it is a good idea to cook on low for 2-3 hours or high for 1-2 hours. The pressure cooker is even faster, you can cook the fish stock for 10 minutes with a natural release and cook shellfish stock for 20 minutes, again, with a natural release. If you combine fish and shellfish, cook it for the longer time of shellfish.

If you are using a slow cooker, you can cook other bones for broth for 12-24 hours, the full 24 hours is preferable. Some internet sources will tell you to cook for longer than this but it is a matter of diminishing returns. There is a point beyond which more minerals cannot be leached from the bones and long boiling will require adding additional water to replace what boils off. It is sufficient to cook for 12 hours and best at 24 hours and longer than that simply just adds complication without reward. When you strain the broth, you will find that the bones simply crumble in the strainer, and this is a sign that all the beneficial nutrition is now in the broth.

Using these longer cooking times, in order to protect the surface that the cooker rests on, use a thick, wooden cutting board underneath it. This is especially important if you have a laminate countertop, these are glued to the surface of your counter and the glue is heat activated. The cooker can heat the glue and cause lifting, especially true if you leave the cooker over a seam. If you placed the cooker directly on the surface and later notice lifting, immediately cover it with a heavy cutting board and top it with something heavy, a large pot filled with water, for example. Leave it to sit for a full 24 hours before checking. If you acted quickly, while the surface was warm, this will often fix it. If you did not act quickly and the laminate is lifting up, place the cooker back over the area and fill it with water, and set it on high. Once the counter is warm, place the wooden cutting board and weight.

Electric pressure cookers are incredibly fast when it comes to preparing bone broths. They work by raising the boiling point of water and this hotter water cooks faster. By preventing the steam from escaping once the liquid is at a boil, they increase the air pressure inside the pot, and this force on the surface of the water causes the water to boil at much higher temperatures before turning into steam. It works in the same way that going down to lower altitudes raises the boiling point, there is less air pushing down on the surface of the water on the summit of Mount Everest than there is in Death Valley because there is simply more atmosphere above the surface of the ground. This affects the boiling point dramatically. On the stovetop, water boils at 212F at sea level but back where I grew up in Colorado in the Mile High City, it boils at 202F. Travel up to Mount Everest, water will boil at just 162F[52]. In a pressure cooker, it boils at about 250F[53]. This dramatically changes the time it takes to make perfect bone broth. Whereas a slow cooker takes 24 hours, a pressure cooker can accomplish this in a fraction of the time. When making bone broth using a mix of bones (other than fish and shellfish), it only takes two hours to achieve the same result.

While not a cooking vessel, a good strainer is important. Look for a fine metal screen type strainer which will catch more of the bone matter after cooking. If there is meat, don't bother saving it, it has served its purpose and has neither flavor nor nutrition, just throw it out. A good screen-style strainer will have reinforcement along the sides, sturdy handles, and often a base to allow it to rest in a large bowl and will be very large. Place it in a bowl and either rest it on the bottom or set the handles over the sides. It is easier to start transferring the broth using a large ladle until the pot is emptied enough to make it lighter and easier to handle. Carefully pour your bone broth into this and allow it to strain before adding additional liquid. If you have a very large amount of broth,

---

[52] Accessed on 10/16/21 https://www.pewresearch.org/fact-tank/2015/09/14/does-waters-boiling-point-change-with-altitude-americans-arent-sure/

[53] Accessed on 10/16/21 https://www.exploratorium.edu/food/pressure-cooking#:~:text=When%20you%20cook%20in%20a,C%20(25 0%C2%BOF).

you might need to remove the strainer and discard the bones before moving it to another bowl.

ADJUNCTS

There is no need to add vegetables to your bone broth. They tend to muddy the flavor overall and don't add much to the nutrition, given the extended cooking time. You can add salt but it is better not to because having no salt means that you don't run the risk of having it become too salty when other foods are added or if you decide to boil it down to concentrate it. You can add peppercorns or some bay leaves or even aromatics like onion or garlic but these are optional and while good, they are not actually necessary. One good addition is an acid like lemon juice or various mild vinegars like white, white wine, or apple cider. If added to the cooking water, this promotes the breakdown of the bones and adds what is known as a "high note" that makes the broth more appealing. Add a tablespoon for every two quarts of the cooking water. In a large crock cooker, this is two tablespoons. You might want to taste and consider adding another teaspoon or two once the broth is finished. It makes a surprising difference. This is also the time to add salt to taste but do so in very small amounts and after you've added the acid, you will find that you need less salt once the flavor is brightened with a little acid.

Storing Bone Broth

An important note is that this broth is very, very hot. Be sure to elevate it from the counter using a firm trivet and cover it with a cloth to allow it to cool but stay clean. Heat rises and a lid will trap that heat but the cloth will allow it to dissipate. If you want to minimize laundry, use a splatter screen to cover the bowl, the kind that is used for frying foods. This could be washed in a dishwasher. Choose a trivet not only to protect your countertop but to allow room for air to circulate underneath it, one with some small legs and perhaps some open grillwork, so the broth will cool faster. Keep it far back on the counter and do not move it until it is cool because of the risk of spilling. Hot broth can cause serious burns and large bowls can be tempting to look into so be very careful around children. I always place a barrier of some kind such as a rolled towel to prevent accidental touching. Keep children and pets away from the broth until it is cool enough to serve, refrigerate, or freeze.

Unless you are immediately making a pot of soup, you will need to store at least some of the resulting broth. There are a few considerations to remember. It is critical to cool it and do so as quickly as possible to prevent pathogens. It is also important not to place it in the freezer while very warm because it can cause other foods to warm which can bring the surfaces of these foods to enter the danger zone of bacterial growth. Freezers have their own risks to consider for storage. Many a home cook has shattered glass jars of broth stored in the freezer and many more have struggled with plastic resealable bags that froze around other items in the freezer to make a seemingly impenetrable shield.

Once the broth is cooler, it can be transferred to glass canning jars which better tolerate higher temperatures. A canning funnel and a large ladle can help make it neater to do. Remember to fill no more than ¾ full if you want to later freeze. Water expands when frozen. These jars can be cooled faster than a large bowl in the refrigerator and can either be later processed again to be frozen or simply used as is.

Another benefit to refrigerating the broth is that it is easier to remove the fat, if necessary. The fats in bone broth provide calories that can be helpful for people who already have difficulty eating sufficient calories. It is also important to mention that vitamins A, D, E, and K are fat-soluble and require a certain amount of fat in the diet to absorb them. That said, some people are necessarily on a fat-reduced diet, such as those with digestive disorders and you should "skim" or reduce or eliminate the fat. Fat will rise to the top of the jars and solidify in a waxy layer that can be lifted off. You could discard this; I feed this to my poultry as a regular source of fat in their diets. If you have made stock using chicken bones, the traditional way of making dumplings for soup is to use this fat instead of oils or butter. The resulting dumplings have a far better flavor and it is definitely worth trying.

Once they have cooled thoroughly and are set and gelatinous, the jars could be transferred to the freezer, without lids, and kept upright until frozen. Do not add lids until completely frozen to allow the broth to expand and do not skip the step of cooling in the fridge. Broth can expand unevenly as it cools and crack the jars. Frozen jars are still very vulnerable to shattering because they become more brittle when cold and they are very heavy. If you plan to store glass jars in the freezer, use solid plastic bins to store them. Look for the kind with solid sides and bottoms that do not have holes because those holes will allow the glass to sift through if you have a broken jar. You can find these at discount and dollar stores. This is not my preferred method because it is so common to shatter glass.

You can also transfer the broth to plastic jars to be more safely stored but be sure it is completely cool to prevent the leaching of undesirable flavors and compounds from the plastic. If you are reusing food containers for storage, be sure to add a layer of plastic cling wrap to prevent the broth from drying out in the freezer. When you need the broth, thaw in the fridge overnight.

Silicon muffin trays set on a firm cookie sheet to make them more stable will also work well and is my preferred method. Their small size increases the surface area which helps them to cool faster. Ladle the hot broth into the muffin cups and transfer the sheet with the muffin tray on it into the fridge. Once they have cooled and are jelly-like, it is easy to transfer to the freezer. Frozen cubes can be popped out to be kept in plastic containers or resealable bags. This small size works well for having quick and easy servings of broth ready for your loved one. You can set a cube in a covered bowl in the fridge overnight to thaw and it will be ready the next day.

You can also transfer the cooled broth to resealable bags. Set each back down on the counter and smooth out the broth to fill the bag and be as level as possible. Wipe the bags down to prevent them from freezing together because of any moisture trapped between the bags, then stack these in a rectangular metal cake pan, then smooth them out once again. Set this in the freezer and when the broth is fully frozen, you can take them out of the pan and they will separate without trouble and be easier to store. These are lighter and less vulnerable to breaking than jars if you want to store larger quantities of broth for making soups later. When you need broth later, set the bag down in a cake pan to catch any leaks and thaw in the fridge overnight.

Using Bone Broth

There are nearly endless uses for broth! There are so many ways to serve bone broth beyond soups and stews. Warmed bone broth is excellent as it is for sipping in a mug. It hydrates with more calories, vitamins, minerals, and protein than water or juice without negatively affecting blood sugar because it is naturally low in carbohydrates. It is especially useful to provide additional nourishment to children, the elderly, and very ill people who might fill up on water or other beverages which can leave little room for food. For those unable to eat solid foods, it is delicious and nourishing as it is but, in a pinch, a more substantial snack can be made by dissolving crackers in it. This is helpful to remember for those who have surgery on their teeth, mouth, and throat.

It is also very useful for those on severely limited diets. Bone broth is also useful as a replacement for the water used to cook grains, beans, and pulses to add additional nutrition. Some kidney patients who live on fluid-restricted diets, particularly those who are also on protein-restricted diets, can benefit from the replacement of water with nutrient-dense bone broth. For those on mechanically and GI soft diets, using bone broth to puree foods adds more nutrition and better flavor than using water alone.

Bone broth can also be used in gelatins and

other stabilized foods to help people with motion or swallowing disruptions who need foods that are firmer without being harder. Used to make gravies, broth can add moisture to foods that would otherwise be too dry for some patients. For those who cannot have or have limited dairy intake, bone broth makes an excellent substitution in savory quick breads, polenta and other porridges, as well as mashed sweet, yellow, or white potatoes. Broth can replace the water in rice and cauliflower rice which adds more nutrition and flavor than water alone. Be sure to check the Soups and Stews as well as the Gelatins and Aspics sections for specific recipes.

CHAPTER FOUR: SOUPS AND STEWS

"At the Last Judgment I shall not be asked whether I was successful in my ascetic exercises, nor how many bows and prostrations I made. Instead, I shall be asked, Did I feed the hungry, clothe the naked, visit the sick and the prisoners. That is all I shall be asked." Mother Maria of Paris

BEING ATTACHED TO A MONASTERY, I spend a lot of time cooking for monks. Without wives or mothers to fuss over them, I happily step into that role. In my introduction, I told you about a creamed carrot and ginger soup I made for a monk recovering from oral surgery. I still call it Soupe Alexander, and it is a regular part of my repertoire. It has a special place in my heart and you can find the recipe here.

Creamed soups are warm and filling but also soothing. They are gentle on the mouth and throat and can be made to be gentle on the digestive system. Creamed soups are a back bone of nourishing recovery foods. These can be made with a wide variety of vegetables which can make for a broader eating experience. Some of the easiest vegetables to work with, ones which work for a large variety of diets, include mushrooms, potatoes, carrots, sweet potato, and butternut squash. As long as patients are not on GI soft diets, you can also incorporate onion and garlic. One of the surprising foods that one can add into most diets is small amounts of ginger root. A tablespoon or even three of finely grated ginger root adds a lot of depth to a soup. This adds complexity and even a little heat without causing heartburn and it won't ferment in the digestive track. Other nice options include broccoli and cauliflower but these are not always permitted. If your loved one has been told to limit dairy, substitute full-fat coconut milk for the amount of cream asked for in the recipe.

Remember that convalescing people with difficulty eating need sufficient fat and protein. Greek yogurt adds a nice tang and a good amount of protein but will not be as creamy as sour cream. You can also mix half and half of any of the fat options. Half cream and half yogurt will be tangy, creamy, and have a higher protein content. Half coconut milk and half dairy can provide a rich dairy flavor without consuming all the day's allowance of dairy.

If onion is permitted, one cup of the vegetables can be onion or leek which adds a lot of flavors. If onions are not allowed, the slices can be kept very large and removed after cooking. This imparts flavor without causing digestive upset. Onion is one of a group of aromatic, beautiful smelling and delicious ingredients that add depth and flavor but there are others that do not cause upset.

- Carrots
- Ginger
- Onions/Leeks
- Garlic
- Celery

When you have to avoid onions, garlic, and leeks, it can be helpful to incorporate carrots, ginger, and celery as a way of adding deep flavor when other seasonings are not on table.

CREAMED VEGETABLE SOUP BASE

This is a basic soup based that allows you to use whatever vegetables are permitted in the diet as well as whatever sort of creamy addition is allowed. Half sour cream and half Greek yogurt is a great option for creaminess but also more protein. If you are caring for a loved one on a puree diet, a stick blender is enormously helpful. When someone asks what you need, ask for one of these. It makes purees and soups so much easier.
- 4 cups chopped mixed vegetables, tightly packed (perhaps divided)
- 3 Tablespoon olive oil
- 4 cups broth, homemade or prepared but not from instant

- 1 ½ cups sour cream, plain Greek yogurt, or whole fat coconut milk

Possible additions:
- one half onion, peeled
- One split and rinsed leek
- 2-4 garlic cloves
- 1 piece of ginger root equal to half your thumb

Mix the vegetables, additions, and olive oil and roast in on a low sided sheet pan at 400 until the pieces can be cut with a fork. This depends on a little on the size of the pieces that you use but could be 20-40 minutes but do stir every fifteen minutes. Once they are softened, add them to your soup pot and add the broth. Simmer for 20 minutes. Transfer to a blender to process in batches or use a stick blender in the pot. Once the soup is completely smooth, add the sour cream, yogurt, or coconut milk. Season with salt and pepper as desired and allowed.

SOUPE ALEXANDER

(CARROT & GINGER CREAMED SOUP)

Russian monks do not eat meat, so his soups were always made using fish and shrimp broth. When he had his mouth surgery, it was a fast. I made this soup for dear Monk Alexander so he could have something warm and soft and soothing for his mouth. Being stoic, he would not budge on the dairy, so I made it dairy free with coconut milk instead. I can promise, however, this soup is delightful with chicken broth and sour cream. This is a larger batch that could be used as a family meal but can easily but cut in half. The fat in the sour cream makes this a good soup for freezing because it won't become grainy when it thaws. Just pop in the fridge overnight and warm before serving.

- 5 pounds carrots, rough chopped
- 2 leeks, split and rinsed
- ⅔ cup olive oil
- 1 piece of ginger, a size about the same as your thumb
- 6 cloves garlic
- 2 quarts bone broth or shrimp broth
- Salt and pepper to taste, if using
- 16 ounces sour cream (or 2 cans of full fat coconut milk if dairy-free)

Preheat oven to 400F. Toss the carrots, leek, and ginger with oil and place on a sheet pan. Roast 15 minutes and then give it a stir. Add the garlic and stir again. Return to the oven for 5-10 minutes until garlic is fragrant. Transfer to a large Dutch oven and add broth. Simmer for another 20 minutes. Process in batches to puree or use a stick blender. After it is smooth, add the sour cream and seasoning and whisk until well combined.

CHICKEN AND DUMPLINGS STEW

This is admittedly a more difficult way to make this soup, but it is well worth the effort. If you are trying to manage your time and efforts, this can be made with a store-bought broth and a rotisserie chicken which makes it more doable. Save the bones and use them to make a batch of broth later. This stew can be tolerated by a variety of diets and can be enjoyed by the whole family which makes is a wonderful family meal. Having to prepare two separate meals is hard on the sick room cook but it is also hard for convalescents to watch others eat food that they cannot. To accommodate eating difficulties, chop the vegetables very finely.

Soup

- 6 bone-in chicken thighs, skin on
- 2 tablespoons olive oil
- 4 celery stalks, chopped
- 4 large carrots, peeled and chopped
- 1 onion, sliced (omit for those with heartburn and leave whole for GI soft diets)
- 4 garlic cloves, chopped (omit for those with heartburn and leave whole for GI soft diets)
- 4 bay leaves

- ½ teaspoon rubbed sage
- ¼ cup white wine (or 1 tablespoon apple cider vinegar and 3 tablespoons broth)
- 2 quarts broth, homemade or store-bought
- Salt and pepper, as allowed and desired

Dumplings

- 1 ⅓ cups all-purpose flour
- 2 teaspoons baking powder
- ¾ teaspoon salt (if allowed)
- ⅔ cup heavy whipping cream (or substitute the fat from the top of the chicken broth, this is very traditional)

In a large heavy bottomed Dutch oven, heat the olive oil over medium high until shimmering. Sprinkle salt and pepper over the breasts, if using, and add to bottom of pot with skin side facing down. Allow to cook until the skin is brown and releases, that is when it no longer sticks to the pot. Lift slightly with tongs and if it sticks, wait another minute. Once they release easily, transfer to a plate. Add the celery, carrots, onion, and garlic, if using. If you will need to remove the onion and garlic because you are feeding someone on a GI diet, leave peel but leave whole and add these when directed). Brown these for ten minutes. Deglaze with the wine or the apple cider vinegar and broth.

If using a rotisserie chicken, shred the chicken first. Then brown the vegetables and deglaze before adding the meat into the pot. Reserve the bones for broth.

Add the chicken and the broth as well as the sage, bay leaves, and broth, and cover with lid. If you will need to remove the onions and garlic, add them now. Place in the oven, set it for 350F, and let it simmer for 30 minutes. Do not turn off the oven.

Remove the pot from oven. This is the time to remove the bay leaves, onion, and garlic. If no one is on a GI soft diet, the onions are garlic can be left in the stew. Remove the chicken thighs and shred but save skin and bones for broth; return the meat to the pot. If using rotisserie chicken, you won't need to do this because you will have already shredded the chicken. Prepare the dumplings.

Whisk the dumpling flour, salt, and baking soda together and work in the whipping cream just until combined. If using cold chicken fat, use a fork to work the fat into the dough. Drop by large spoonfuls over the surface of the soup. Bake, covered, at 350F for 18-20 minutes.

BEEF AND BARLEY SOUP

This soup is wonderful with the addition of beef, but it is still delicious without it. This soup is fairly quick to make without too many fussy steps. If you are cooking for a GI soft or low residue diet, substitute rice for the barley.

- ½ pound ground beef (can be omitted)
- 8 ounces mushrooms (16 ounces if not using beef)
- 4 celery stalks, chopped
- 4 large carrots, peeled and chopped
- 1 onion, sliced (omit for those with heartburn and leave whole for GI soft diets)
- 4 garlic cloves, chopped (omit for those with heartburn and leave whole for GI soft diets)
- 4 bay leaves
- ½ teaspoon rubbed sage
- ¼ cup red wine (can be omitted)
- 2 quarts broth, homemade or store-bought
- Salt and pepper, as allowed and desired
- ¾ cup pearled barley (GI soft and low residue: substitute white rice)

In a heavy Dutch oven, brown the ground beef until no longer pink and remove to a pie plate. In the same pot and without draining, add the mushrooms, celery, and carrots as well as the onion and garlic unless you are following a GI soft diet when it will be added later. Brown these things thoroughly, sprinkling with salt and pepper, if using. If the beef is fatty and there is a lot of grease in the pot, use a slotted spoon to remove the vegetables to the same pie plate as the beef and drain the pot. Return the beef and vegetables to the pot and add the wine. Stir well before adding the broth. If omitting the wine, add all of the broth at this time. Those on a GI soft diet can add the large pieces of onion and garlic now. After the soup cooks, do not forget to remove them. Add the barley or rice and bring to a boil, turn down to the lowest setting, and then cover. Cook for 35 minutes for pearled barley but only 20 minutes for rice. Remove the onion and garlic, if necessary, before serving.

CREAMY MUSHROOM SOUP

This is one of those delightful soups that most people never have the chance to eat because we are so used to eating the canned variety. It never ceases to amaze me just how delicious it is when cooked from scratch. It really doesn't take long at all to make this soup and it is so worth it. If you don't have homemade bone broth, store bought will do just fine. In the end, this soup is a little different every time because the flavor will change depending on the mushrooms and broth used but it will always be deeply satisfying. If you need to feed someone on a pureed diet, this soup will work beautifully well. It also does not have any fermenting vegetables that are not allowed on GI soft or low residue diets.

- 16 oz fresh mushrooms, button or crimini or whatever is available
- 3 tablespoons butter
- 3 quarts bone broth, any variety of homemade or store-bought
- 2 cups sour cream (dairy-free use one can full-fat coconut milk)
- Several springs of fresh parsley
- Salt and pepper to taste (if allowed)

Melt the butter in a large Dutch oven and add the mushrooms and stir only once. Cook over medium high heat until the mushrooms are shrunken, dark, and almost syrupy. Do not stir them again for five minutes to allow the mushrooms to weep. It will take 10-15 minutes over all to cook them down until they weep all their liquid and it evaporates. They will be almost sticky looking. Add the parsley and the broth, cover, bring to a boil, and turn down to simmer for 10 minutes. Stir in the sour cream and add salt and pepper, if using. If you will puree the soup, skip the parsley because it will affect the overall color.

SOPA DE ARROZ

(MEXICAN RICE SOUP)

This soup is really just a very overblown rice dish and was a staple of my childhood. I still make it at least four or five times a month. It is easily blended for a pureed meal but it is very soft which makes it a good transition food for those graduating to a more solid diet. It is also very good with shredded or diced meat but tastes wonderful even without.

- 3 cups short-grain white rice
- 1 sweet onion, sliced
- 6 tomatoes, large dice (for low residue, GI soft substitute one small can of tomato paste)
- 4-6 cloves of garlic, chopped
- 4 tablespoons olive oil
- 2 quarts bone broth, homemade or store-bought
- Salt and pepper, to taste (if allowed)

In a large, heavy Dutch oven, brown the rice and onion in oil over medium-high heat. The rice will initially be slightly transparent and eventually become opaque and then it will toast. Stir constantly and keep the rice moving. When it is opaque, add the garlic. Continue to stir and brown until the rice begins to get slightly toasty colored and is fragrant. Add the tomatoes and stir until they begin to break down. Don't worry about the skins, it will be fine. If cooking for a low residue or GI soft diet, add the tomato paste. Add the broth and turn the heat up to high. Once it is at a solid boil, turn the heat down very low and cover. Allow the rice to cook for 20 minutes and serve.

CHAPTER FIVE: GELATIN FOODS

"For if God does not for a moment tire of giving us good things, how can we tire of thanking him for these good things?" St Nicolai Velimirovich

GELATIN IS A GOOD SOURCE of protein, and it firms up other foods, making it a boon to those who have trouble swallowing. Most Americans are only familiar with the boxes of sweet and flavored gelatin with artificial coloring, but in the same area of the supermarket, you can find boxes of unflavored gelatin. This gelatin comes in premeasured envelopes and recipes are usually written to accommodate the whole envelope. With more than six grams of protein[54] in every envelope, incorporating more gelatin into the diet of your loved one can help them regain weight and muscle mass that can be lost during convalescence. Every gram counts during recovery, and gelatin can be a great way to add more protein without the difficulty of chewing that meat can cause.

One of the great things about gelatin is that it is very kid-friendly. If you are caring for a

---

[54] Accessed on 3/2/22
https://www.knoxgelatine.com/basics.htm

child, you can treat them with fruit juice gelatins and smoothies and know that they are getting much needed protein. Smoothies and pops are especially good following mouth and throat surgery because the cold temperature can be soothing to sore tissues. If your loved one has had recent injuries or surgery or you need to monitor them for bleeding, be sure to make gelatins that don't include red ingredients.

Gelatin makes a solid base for additional ingredients to make it both more appealing and nutritious. So long as you follow the dietary guidelines of your loved one, you can create a lot of variety using the basic recipes as a base.

Fruit set in gelatin is a classic dish and can be made appropriate for many diets. When adding fruit, it is important to know that some fruits contain enzymes that react with the protein in gelatin and that will prevent it from firming up. Cooking stops this process so using canned versions of these things makes it a quicker process; otherwise, you will have to cook the fruit first. Frozen versions of fruit with enzymes also won't work, the heat is very necessary to break down this enzyme.

Fruit that Prevents Gelatin from Setting	
Pineapple (use canned instead)	Ginger

Kiwi	Papaya
Figs	Guava (use prepared versions)

There are lots of options to use instead, see the list below. If you still want these foods, choose canned or you will have to cook them first. You don't have to restrict your additions to just fruit, some vegetables work very well with fruit juice and can add interest as well as nutrition.

Fruits and Vegetables that Work Well in Gelatins	
Fresh peaches	Fresh grapes
Fresh plums	Fresh orange segments
Fresh melon	Canned pineapple
Fresh strawberries	Canned fruit cocktail
Fresh apples	Cucumber (drained after chopping)
Grated carrot (press out the liquid) or sliced	Fresh raspberries, blackberries,

cooked or canned (for some diets)	blueberries

Bone broth-based gelatin, or aspic, is also delicious with additions, but these are usually vegetable, meat, poultry, fish, and hard-boiled eggs. While these kinds of dishes are not as common in North American kitchens, they are a staple of Slavic cooking. With the highly nutritious base of bone broth and other highly nutritious additions, they are a fantastic food for those who are recovering from injury, illness, and surgery.

Depending on the dietary needs of your loved one, you might need to cook the vegetables ahead of time. Prepare them according to the vegetable puree section just stopping short of the puree step. If you don't have time for this, choose low sodium canned vegetables. There is only so much time for cooking. If you have leftover meat, you can chop it finely to add to this dish. You can also use low sodium canned versions of plain canned meats such as chicken, beef, or pork. You can even use canned fish like tuna, mackerel, and salmon. Chopped hard-boiled eggs are also a good addition and they are great for both mechanically soft and GI soft diets. See the entree section for cooking those. Once you have tried this dish, you can expand and add in things like onion and garlic which are delicious but not always appropriate for a convalescent diet.

Additions to Aspic	
Chopped, cooked lean beef and pork	Grated Carrots
Chopped chicken, skin removed	Sliced, cooked carrot
Chopped canned beef, pork, chicken	Canned carrot pieces
Chopped cooked fish, skin removed	Fresh or frozen peas
Chopped, drained fish with skin and bones removed	Canned peas
Chopped hard-boiled eggs	

BASIC FRUIT JUICE GELATIN

- 3 1/2 cups allowed fruit juice, divided
- 2 envelopes of gelatin (such as Knox)

Using a heatproof bowl, pour in one cup of the juice then sprinkle the gelatin over the top. Allow it to soften for two minutes, it needs to swell so that it can dissolve in the hot liquid and properly set. Take the remainder of the juice and bring it to a boil. Pour over the softened gelatin mixture and stir constantly until the gelatin is well combined or about two minutes. Transfer to a mold and refrigerate for four hours or until firm. This makes a firmer gelatin so this can be set into silicon ice cube molds to make a more entertaining food. Set the mold into warm water but be sure that it does not go over the rim of the mold. Allow it to sit for only a minute and then press a plate over the top. Gently flip so the plate is on the bottom and then remove the mold. Keep the gelatin covered in the fridge.

BASIC CREAMY GELATIN

You can also add plain or flavored Greek yogurt to your fruit juice gelatins. Not only do these look more substantial, but the yogurt adds extra calories and even more protein, which can help patients recover lost weight. This mixture can also be used for reluctant eaters, using a flavored Greek yogurt that complements the juice flavor. You can also add fruit and vegetable additions to make a more interesting dish.

- 1 ½ cups allowed fruit juice, divided
- 2 cups plain or flavored Greek yogurt
- 2 envelopes of gelatin (such as Knox)

Using a heatproof bowl, pour in 3/4 cup of the juice then sprinkle the gelatin over the top. Allow it to soften for two minutes, it needs to swell so that it can dissolve in the hot liquid and properly set. Take the remaining ¾ cup of juice and bring to a boil, a microwave is good for this. Pour over the softened gelatin mixture and stir constantly until the gelatin is well combined or about two minutes. Add the yogurt one cup at a time and mix well after each addition. Transfer to a mold and refrigerate for four hours or until firm. This makes a firmer gelatin so this can be set into silicon ice cube molds to make a more entertaining food. Set the mold into warm water but be sure that it does not go over the rim of the mold. Allow it to sit for only a minute and then press a plate over the top. Gently flip so the plate is on the bottom and then remove the mold. Keep the gelatin covered in the fridge.

FRUIT STUDDED GELATIN

- 1 batch Basic Fruit Juice Gelatin or Basic Creamy Fruit Gelatin Base
- 2 cups of finely chopped or grated fruit or vegetables

Mix the gelatin according to the original instructions in this book and set it in a bowl in the fridge for an hour and perhaps up to an hour and a half. When it is slightly jiggly and about the texture of unbeaten egg whites, then it is ready to add the fruit or vegetable. While it sets in the fridge, prepare the additions. See the lists above for appropriate fruit and vegetable additions. Be careful to not introduce any more liquid so drain anything that might become juicy by setting it in a sieve over a bowl. With carrots, you might need to press slightly with the back of a spoon to encourage more liquid to drain. Mix the additions with gelatin and transfer to a mold. Refrigerate for four hours or until firm before serving.

BASIC ASPIC

- 4 cups bone broth, seasoned to taste with salt, divided
- 1-2 envelopes of gelatin (such as Knox)
- 1 loaf pan

If using store-bought broth or shellfish broth, you will need to use two envelopes of gelatin in order to ensure that it sets up firmly. If using homemade broth according to the instructions in this book, you will only need one envelope. Many aspics add meat or vegetables to the mold which add variety and nutrition but they aren't appropriate for those on a clear diet. This is a simple aspic that uses just well-strained broth which makes it safe for the clear liquid diet. Using a heat-proof bowl, sprinkle the gelatin over one cup of cool broth. Allow it to soften for two minutes, it needs to swell so that it can dissolve in the hot liquid and properly set. Take the remainder of the broth and bring it to a boil. Pour over the softened gelatin mixture and stir constantly until the gelatin is well combined or about two minutes. Transfer to the loaf pan and refrigerate for four hours or until firm. The homemade broth in particular will be set up firm enough that it can be sliced and served. Serving the food in a slightly different way can help the mood so much. If the broth is served at most meals hot, having something deeply nourishing but which does not look like a beverage is a welcome change of pace.

KHOLODETS, STUDDED ASPIC

This dish is very common in Slavic households but less known by Americans, which is unfortunate. It is an incredibly nourishing food and is ideal for convalescents. As long as the additions are chopped finely to allow them to be eaten easily, you can add a wide variety of foods to your final dish. Because it can be made ahead of time and served as needed, this can help the harried sickroom cook provide something high in protein when time and strength are in short supply. If you want to help with feeding a recovering loved one in another household, bone broth-based foods are always a great idea.

- 1 batch Basic Aspic
- 2 cups of additions, see list above for suggestions

Mix the aspic according to the original instructions in this book and set it in a bowl in the fridge for an hour and perhaps up to an hour and a half. When it is slightly jiggly and about the texture of unbeaten egg whites, then it is ready to add the fruit or vegetable. While it sets in the fridge, prepare the additions. See the lists above for appropriate meat, fish, and vegetable additions. Be careful to not introduce any more liquid so drain anything that might become juicy by setting it in a sieve over a bowl, this is particularly true of canned fish and meat. Grated carrots might need to be pressed slightly with the back of a spoon to encourage more liquid to drain. Mix the additions with gelatin and transfer to a mold. Refrigerate for four hours or until firm before serving.

PANNA COTTA

Despite its very fancy pedigree and Italian name, this just means "cooked cream". Basically, it is a delightful, creamy dairy custard set with gelatin and prepared very similarly to other gelatin dishes. It is very nutrient-dense making it an excellent food for people struggling to recover lost weight during illness. It is also mechanically soft and GI soft though some GI soft diets require a low-fat version. The low-fat version is made with whole milk which might seem like it is not actually low fat but it is important to note that whole milk is only 4% fat while heavy cream is 40%. This is a 90% reduction in fat.

- 1 envelope gelatin
- 2 tablespoons water
- 3 cups heavy whipping cream (lower fat option: whole milk)
- ⅓ cup honey or maple syrup
- 2 teaspoons vanilla extract

Bloom the gelatin in the water in a small pot, just sprinkle it over the top of the water so that it can absorb water and soften so that it will fully dissolve in the cream or milk. Allow it to sit for two minutes and then warm it on the stove over medium heat and stir until the gelatin is completely dissolved. Remove from heat and set aside. In a medium saucepan, heat the cream or milk with the honey or maple syrup just until it begins to steam. You will need to stir constantly so that it does not burn or boil over. Use a wooden spoon because the handle will not get hot. Once it is steaming, turn off the heat and stir in the gelatin, and whisk until well combined. You can pour it into a one-quart mold or into 4 one-cup ramekins or 8 half-cup ramekins. You can also use a silicone cupcake tray. Cool to room temperature and then chill in the fridge for at least six hours or overnight. Once they are removed from their molds, they are firmly set and will be firm for serving.

FRUIT SMOOTHIES

Gelatin not only thickens smoothies, which can help people who need thicker foods, but it adds more than 6 grams of protein per envelope. When helping a loved one regain lost weight and muscle mass, every gram of protein counts. This recipe works with any frozen fruit that is allowed. Be sure to avoid red foods following surgery as well as acidic fruits. Strawberries are a popular option but they have lots of small seeds which can be problematic for some patients. Frozen bananas, peaches, and mangos are often well tolerated by most diets so these are great options. This smoothie is also very easy to make dairy-free for those who cannot have dairy.

- 1 envelop of gelatin
- ¼ cup water
- 6 ice cubes
- 1 ½ cups of cold milk or dairy-free milk substitute

- 2-3 tablespoons of honey, to taste
- 2 teaspoons of vanilla
- 1 ½ - 1 ¾ cups of frozen fruit, do not thaw (choose banana for GI soft and low residue diets)

Pour the water into a microwave-safe coffee mug and sprinkle the gelatin over the water to allow it to bloom or soften. Let this sit for two minutes and then microwave on high for 25 seconds to heat the gelatin. Pour into a blender and the ice cubes, process until the ice is melted. Add milk, honey, vanilla, and process until combined. Add the fruit a bit at a time until it is at the proper consistency. More fruit will yield a thinner smoother and less fruit will make a thicker one. Serve immediately.

MOLDED SALMON SALAD

Molded salads get a bad rap because they are considered old-fashioned but they are a great way to introduce protein to people who need a smooth but firm texture and can be served cold. Having lots of options for foods of different temperatures as well as being able to pull something from the fridge to eat at the last minute is a boon to a harried caregiver. This molded salad would have been popular sixty years ago but really deserves a place at the modern table.

- 1 envelope gelatin
- ½ cup broth, use the recipe in this book or store-bought
- 1 1/2 cup Greek yogurt
- 1 (14 ounces) can of salmon, drained and flaked with a fork (skin and bones removed for those on a more restrictive soft diet)
- 2 hard-boiled eggs, chopped
- 2 tbsp chopped fresh dill (or 1 tablespoon dried)
- Salt and pepper, optional

Add the broth to a coffee cup and sprinkle the gelatin over the cold broth to allow it to bloom or absorb moisture to soften. Let it stand for two minutes. Microwave on high for 25 seconds to soften the gelatin, stir well, then pour into a medium bowl and add the Greek yogurt, whisking well with a dinner fork. It will seem oversized but it will provide space for the other ingredients. Chill in the fridge for about 30 minutes, stirring every ten minutes. The mixture should resemble unbeaten egg whites. Fold in the salmon, eggs, and dill. Salt and pepper can be added now, as much as is permitted and desired. Transfer to a one-quart mold and refrigerate for about four hours or until set. Unmold and serve.

FUDGE POPS

Those popular fudge pops are a go-to for mouth surgery, but they often completely lack any nutrition. I know how much my daughter craved them when she had her tonsils removed. I wanted to not just soothe her throat but make sure she had something that was nourishing. This is the perfect option if you find yourself in the same situation. I plan on making lots of these for when two of my teenage sons have their wisdom teeth removed this summer. It does seem like a lot of chocolate syrup but, Greek yogurt is very tangy and it is important to include this variety to have the added protein. If your loved one has to be dairy-free, follow the dairy-free option.

- 1 envelop gelatin
- 3/4 cup cold whole milk or dairy-free milk substitute
- 1 cup Greek yogurt (dairy-free: the cream from one can of full-fat coconut milk)
- 2/3 cup chocolate syrup, sugar-free if desired

In a coffee cup, sprinkle the gelatin over cold milk. Let this sit for two minutes to allow the gelatin to bloom or begin to soften. Microwave the milk for one minute, stirring halfway through. The milk should be very hot and the gelatin absorbed. If not, return to the microwave for another 15-20 seconds. Pour into a blender and add the other ingredients and blend until well combined. Pour into popsicle molds and freeze until solid. The length of time depends on the size of your molds.

CHAPTER SIX: BEVERAGES

"Stand at the brink of despair, and when you see that you cannot bear it anymore, draw back a little, and have a cup of tea."
-Elder Sophrony of Essex

IT MIGHT BE UNEXPECTED to have a section on beverages in a book focused on healing foods and convalescent diets, but it is not only appropriate but actually necessary. As people recover from illness and injury, it is important to stay hydrated. It can be difficult for patients to be aware of their thirst and need for liquids when other pains and symptoms are speaking loudly. Finding appealing things to drink is suddenly very necessary. Elderly patients are especially vulnerable to complications like kidney and urinary tract infections when they don't drink sufficient amounts of water.

For almost all patients, some fluid-restricted kidney patients aside, you should keep a straw cup nearby and regularly encourage your loved one to drink often. It might seem like a better idea to get a large container, especially the jug style with the measurements on the side, but be cautious about this. If the container is very large, it might be unwieldy for children, the elderly, or those who are weak to drink easily. Some patients will choose, either consciously or unconsciously, to avoid drinking rather than asking for help. A smaller container will need to be filled more often but if it can be easily handled, then it means a certain level of independence which can improve overall consumption. If you are caring for an elderly patient or one experiencing weakness, looking for unbreakable drinkware that looks like glass can help maintain a sense of dignity. Don't forget that not all patients will be able to use straws. Commuter cups or soft flexible cups are good solutions for those patients.

It is not just children who respond to brightly colored and printed beverage cups. Providing an array of fun cups to choose from can help your loved one feel like they can exercise some control over their lives and experience some pleasure. If you choose dishwasher-safe cups, it will cut down on the work for you and this is an important consideration. Caregivers have so much on their metaphorical plates and it is important to avoid adding to this.

Much of this section was crafted especially to account for the needs of those on a clear diet even if not all the recipes are appropriate for them. One of the challenges of this intense but short diet is that there is little consideration given to helping those patients know what they can eat and drink. It is not uncommon to feel a sense of panic and worry over what they will eat and a single page of suggestions handed over at the surgery scheduling appointment does little to ease this.

Being able to plan ahead for this and knowing with confidence that you have options can alleviate at least some of the concerns.

FLAVORED DAIRY COFFEE CREAMER

If you are caring for a loved one on a kidney diet, you might have been cautioned about the phosphorus in their diet. Many store-bought coffee creamers have added phosphorus, 100% percent of which is absorbed. This particular coffee creamer is made with heavy whipping cream and simple syrup. Only 80% of the phosphorus in dairy products is absorbed and being combined with the syrup means there is a significant reduction in overall phosphorus. If your loved one is allowed some dairy, this would be a better option.

- ¾ cup granulated sugar
- ¾ cup water
- 2 cups heavy whipping cream
- ¾ teaspoon extract of choice: vanilla, rum, peppermint, hazelnut, chocolate, or almond (which tastes like cherry)

Combine sugar and water in a small saucepan and heat over medium-high heat until the sugar dissolves. It takes only a minute or two. Whisk in the cream and extract and stir well. Transfer to a jar and keep it in the refrigerator. Use within five days.

FLAVORED NON-DAIRY COFFEE CREAMER

Many store-bought coffee creamers have added phosphorus, 100% percent of which is absorbed. If phosphorus is a concern in your loved one's diet, remember that 80% of the phosphorus in dairy products is absorbed. If this is too much for them, a non-dairy version with no added phosphorus is quick and easy to make.

- ¾ cup granulated sugar
- ¾ cup water
- 1 can full-fat coconut milk
- ¾ teaspoon extract of choice: vanilla, rum, peppermint, hazelnut, chocolate, or almond (which tastes like cherry)

Combine sugar and water in a small saucepan and heat over medium-high heat until the sugar dissolves. It takes only a minute or two. Whisk in the canned coconut milk and extract and stir well. Transfer to a jar and keep it in the refrigerator. Use within five days.

HERB INFUSED SIMPLE SYRUP FOR FLAVORING WATER

- ¾ cup granulated sugar
- ¾ cup water
- 2 pencil-sized sprigs of fresh herbs such as basil, rosemary, thyme, mint AND/OR 1 strip of lemon or orange peel about the width of your thumb

Combine all ingredients in a small saucepan and heat over medium-high heat until the sugar dissolves. It takes only a minute or two. Cover and rest for thirty minutes before straining to transfer to a small jar. The syrup will keep in the fridge for four weeks and will readily dissolve in cold or room temperature drinks.

SPICED SIMPLE SYRUP FOR COFFEE OR TEA

- ¾ cup granulated sugar
- ¾ cup water
- 1 strip orange peel about the width of your thumb PLUS one cinnamon stick
- OR
- 1 half vanilla bean, split

Combine all ingredients in a small saucepan and heat over medium-high heat until the sugar dissolves. It takes only a minute or two. Cover and rest for thirty minutes before straining and transferring to a small jar. The syrup will keep in the fridge for four weeks and will readily dissolve in cold or room temperature drinks.

SIMPLE ICED TEA BY THE PITCHER

Sometimes a medical condition limits our choice of beverages. It can be frustrating to avoid sodas and seltzers or caffeinated drinks. Keeping a half-gallon pitcher or jar of tea in the fridge for these times can provide something cool and refreshing when other choices are not available. This tea can be prepared plain or with sweetener and with or without lemon. If your loved one is on a clear diet preparing for medical procedures, making it with sugar with providing some much-needed energy for the short period they are on the diet, provided that they are not also diabetic.

- 6 bags of black tea, perhaps decaffeinated or substitute herbal
- 1-4 tablespoons of sugar, if desired
- 1 strip of lemon peel about the size of your thumb
- 8 cups water, divided
- 1 half-gallon (eight cups) jar or pitcher

In a medium saucepan, combine 4 cups of water, sugar (if using), and lemon peel (if using) and bring to a boil. Remove from heat and add the tea bags. If using black tea, steep for ten minutes. If using herbal tea, steep for fifteen. Remove tea bags but leave peels and allow the tea to cool for one-half hour. Strain and then transfer to pitcher and add enough water to equal eight cups, about four additional cups. Refrigerate. Tea is scalable which means you can cut this recipe in half or double, even triple it with no problems--you only need to change the amounts used. The only change is the cooling time since larger amounts of liquid take longer to cool. Serve this tea cold or heat immediately before serving.

RUSSIAN STYLE TEA BY THE PITCHER

In the 1960s, Americans made a version of this tea using instant sweetened tea and instant orange flavored drink mix which was popular and appealing but this version is so much better. It can be a welcome treat when other beverages are off the menu. It can be served either hot or cold and is easily heated in the microwave. The cold is a lovely thirst quencher, but the hot is so soothing.

- 6 bags of black tea (or substitute herbal)
- 1-4 tablespoons of sugar, if desired

- 3-4 strips of orange or lemon peel or a mix of both
- 2 cinnamon sticks
- 8 cups water, divided
- 1 half-gallon (eight cups) jar or pitcher

In a medium saucepan, combine 4 cups of water, sugar (if using), fruit peel, and cinnamon sticks and bring to a boil. Remove from heat and add the tea bags. If using black tea, steep for ten minutes. If using herbal tea, steep for fifteen. Remove tea bags but leave the peels and cinnamon and allow the tea to cool for one-half hour. Strain and then transfer to pitcher and add enough water to equal eight cups, about four additional cups. Refrigerate. Tea is scalable which means you can cut this recipe in half or double, even triple it with no problems--you only need to change the amounts used. The only change is the cooling time since larger amounts of liquid take longer to cool. Serve this tea cold or heat immediately before serving.

LEMONADE

Ice cold lemonade is a fixture of memories, we know what it is like to have drink it on a hot day even if we have only ever had the mix. This is a delightful beverage to have in the fridge as a way to quench thirst and provide a little variety.

Lemons are high acid so it is important to choose a different beverage if your loved must avoid acidic foods. If your loved one is on a low residue diet, make the version using bottled juice because it is critical to avoid the pulp and zest in the fresh version.

- 1 ½ cups of sugar
- 1 ½ cups of water, plus additional
- 10 Lemons, separate the juice and zest (for low residue: use 1 ½ cup of bottled juice)

In a medium-sized pot, add the sugar, water, and zest and heat over medium to make a flavored simple syrup. If following a low residue diet, you will add the water and sugar and omit the zest. The sugar should dissolve in a minute or two. Allow to cool for fifteen minutes. Transfer the lemon simple syrup to a half-gallon pitcher or jar. Add the lemon juice and enough water to equal a half gallon. Refrigerate until cold and serve.

MEXICAN STYLE HOT CHOCOLATE

In Mexico, hot chocolate is often enjoyed for breakfast. It is far more substantial than American-style cocoa. This will need to be finished in a blender or with a stick blender. This makes the final result smooth and creamy and gives it a little bit of froth. You can buy bricks of Mexican style chocolate for cocoa in the store but this from scratch homemade version is not difficult and worth the effort.

- 2 cups whole milk
- 1 cup heavy whipping cream
- 1 cinnamon stick
- 2 tablespoons honey
- ¼ teaspoon cayenne pepper (omit if you find this too spicy)
- ¼ teaspoon nutmeg
- 1 cup semisweet chocolate chips

In a small pot on the stove over medium-low heat, stir together all the ingredients except the chocolate. Because dairy boils over very easily, you will need to stir constantly. It is a good idea to use a wooden spoon that will not get hot with the long contact. When the mixture is very warm and small bubbles appear at the edge, transfer to a blender, and the chocolate, and process until smooth. If using a stick blender, add the chocolate to the pot and process until smooth. If you are fortunate enough to own a high-powered blender like a Vitamix, you can add all the ingredients at once and set it to the hot soup setting and process.

MULLING SPICES FOR APPLE JUICE, CIDER, OR WINE

A cup of something warm and fragrant can be somehow both stimulating and soothing. This blend of spices will work well for cider but those on a low residue diet or a clear liquid can substitute apple juice. This blend also works well for making spiced sweet wine. While my mother and grandmother are no medical experts, I have found their advice of drinking warm mulled sweet wine to be very helpful when I have had a cold though this advice is best for adults and only those permitted small amounts of alcoholic beverages. Do use a red wine labeled as sweet or it might become bitter when heated. This particular recipe avoids nutmeg which is not appropriate for all diets and means that even those with acid reflux can enjoy this blend.

- 3 cinnamon sticks
- 3 tablespoons cardamom pods
- ¼ cup whole cloves
- 3 tablespoons crystallized ginger

To break the spice, use a spice grinder, but only until it is broken and not powdered. Another option is a zipper seal bag wrapped in a kitchen towel that is beaten with a meat mallet, a rolling pin, or the bottom of a cast-iron pan. The goal is not to make a powdered blend but to break it into small fragments bigger than loose leaf tea. You will need to break the cinnamon, cardamom, and cloves to make smaller pieces that you will use almost like tea. Once they are broken, mix in the ginger and transfer to a small jar to use later.

For Cider or Juice: Add two tablespoons to a quart of juice and heat in a pot over medium heat until steaming. Strain and serve. If fat is allowed, a pat of unsalted butter on each cup is a wonderful addition.

For wine: Use a sweet wine and look for descriptions that include terms like sweet, jammy, and fruity. If using a half-sized bottle, add one heaping tablespoon of spices plus two tablespoons of honey in a medium saucepan and warm over medium heat until steamy. For a standard-sized bottle, add two heaping tablespoons of spices plus ¼ cup of honey and warm over medium heat until steamy. For both amounts, strained before serving. Just as with cider, a pat of unsalted butter on each cup is delicious.

HOT TODDY

This admittedly is an alcoholic drink and not appropriate for children or all adults, but it is very soothing. It can be made without any alcohol and will still be a soothing drink for sore throats. It is my personal go-to for scratchy throats raw from coughing. It can help relax one enough to help with sleep but as with all alcoholic drinks, should be enjoyed in moderation. This particular version starts with a base of herbal tea rather than hot water. My favorite tea for this is peach flavored.

- 1 bag fruity herbal tea or chamomile tea
- 1 cup of boiling water
- 2 tablespoons honey
- 1 cinnamon stick
- 1 lemon wedge
- 1 shot of whiskey or limoncello (alcohol free: substitute one tablespoon lemon juice)

In a deep mug, add the tea bag, honey, cinnamon, and lemon. Steep for 5-8 minutes and then stir in the whisky or limoncello, if desired.

CHAPTER SEVEN: ENTREES

"As salt is needed for all kinds of food, so humility is needed for all kinds of virtues."
-St Isaac the Syrian

IT CAN BE CHALLENGING FOR THE CONVALESCENT to feel like they only ever eat snacks and cannot enjoy meals that the rest of the family is eating. This section has some dishes that can be enjoyed by family and which your recovering loved one can also enjoy. Cooking a single meal that the whole family can eat will help with over-all workload. Some dishes are designed to help you cook ahead so that you can cook once and serve twice so on days when there is more time, you can spend more effort and on days when there is less time, there is something already made.

LOWER PHOSPHORUS WHITE SAUCE MIX

While this is not an entree, it will help with cooking your dinners. If your loved one is on a kidney diet, you might have been warned about the amount of phosphorus in packaged sauce mixes. This is a homemade bulk seasoning so that you can make a healthier alternative that is lower in phosphorus.

- 1 cup powdered milk
- 1 cup powdered coconut milk
- 1 cup all-purpose flour
- 1 tablespoon dried parsley
- ½ teaspoon white pepper

Whisk all ingredients together and keep in a labeled quart jar in the fridge. One-half cup of mix equals a package of white sauce mix. You can also mix one-half cup with a cup of cool water, non-dairy milk, or broth and whisk together, this sauce will thicken with heat.

DAIRY WHITE SAUCE MIX

If you are limiting sodium and phosphorus but do not need to dramatically cut it, this dairy-based white sauce mix is a delicious alternative to powdered mixes found in the store.

- 2 cups powdered milk
- 1 cup all-purpose flour
- 1 tablespoon dried parsley
- 2 teaspoons salt (can be omitted)
- 1 teaspoon white pepper

Whisk all ingredients together and keep in a labeled quart jar in the fridge. One-half cup of mix equals a package of white sauce mix. You can also mix a one-half cup with a cup of cool milk or broth and whisk together; this sauce will thicken with heat.

GENTLE COOKED CEREAL

Sometimes patients need a very bland cooked cereal that will be mild and gentle on their recovering bodies. If you have never cooked dry cereals before, the important thing to remember is to whisk constantly as you slowly add the cereal to the boiling liquid. This recipe offers the option of half milk but the mildest version is made with water. If your loved one needs a barely thickened cereal, use the lower amount given, but if creamy textures are allowed, use the higher amount. You can use any store-bought, finely milled cereal like Farina or Cream of Wheat or even polenta using Mexican maize masa. A little fruit jelly or maple syrup can make this more appealing.

- ¾ cup (or 1 cup) finely milled cooked cereal
- 2 cups water (or one cup water and one cup milk or milk substitute)
- Salt or sugar to taste, if allowed

Combine water and milk, if using both, in a small pan. Over high heat, bring to a boil. Stir while heating, if milk was added. Once at a rolling boil, turn heat down to medium and slowly add the cereal, whisking constantly. Continue to stir until the cereal begins to thicken, about 3-5 minutes. Remove pot from heat.

RICH COOKED CEREAL

Cooked cereals are soft both mechanically and in terms of their gentleness on the gut but they tend to be low protein and short on calories. Some patients need more protein and calories to help in their recovery and this richer version is better for them. Adding eggs to cook cereals increases their caloric content and protein and makes them feel creamier for a more pleasant mouthfeel. This works very well for finely milled cooked cereals like Farina and Cream of Wheat.

- 3 tablespoons butter
- ⅓ cup finely milled cooked cereal
- 1 cup whole milk
- 1 cup heavy cream
- 1 whole egg
- Salt and sugar to taste, if allowed

Place the egg in a small bowl and beat thoroughly. Melt the butter in a small pot and add the uncooked, dry cereal. Brown over medium heat until the mixture smells nutty, about 3-5 minutes. Combine the milk and cream and slowly pour into the pot while whisking constantly. Once it is combined, continue whisking slowly until the cereal begins to thicken, another 3-5 minutes. Remove pot from heat. Add a small spoonful of cooked cereal at a time to the beaten eggs and stir well, a fork works well for this. Continue adding cereal and stirring after every addition until the egg mixture is steaming. Pour the egg mixture back into the pot of cooked cereal and whisk well to combine. This mixture will set up firmly if refrigerated and can be served as a polenta-like cake if firm foods are allowed. If allowed, try topping it with jelly or even a little maple syrup.

GENTLE SCRAMBLED EGGS

- 3 eggs
- 2 Tablespoons warm water
- 1 tablespoon butter

Beat the eggs and the water together before adding to a non-stick pan, this coating is more important for lean eggs than those with cream. You can find ceramic pans if you are avoiding chemical non-stick coatings. Melt the butter in the pan before pouring in the egg mixture. Over medium heat, cook by stirring in small circles.

Adding water to the eggs loosens them without adding additional fat and the result is a softer dish that is easier to eat. Cook just until the eggs are holding together but are not dry, they should appear a little wet and shimmery. Overcooked eggs will shrivel and leave puddles behind. This isn't appetizing but more importantly, it is also harder to eat.

RICH SCRAMBLED EGGS

- 3 eggs
- ¼ cup whipping cream
- 1 tablespoon butter

Beat the eggs and the cream together before adding to a non-stick pan. If you avoid using Teflon, there are good ceramic pans that work beautifully for this. Melt the butter in the pan before pouring in the egg mixture. Over medium heat, cook by stirring in small circles. This recipe includes a higher than the common amount of cream which increases the nutritional density of the food but it also makes a softer final dish that is easier for people to chew and swallow. Cook just until the eggs are holding together but are not dry. They should appear a little wet and shimmery. Overcooked eggs will shrivel and leave puddles behind. This is not only unappetizing, but more importantly, it is also harder to eat.

EASY MACARONI AND CHEESE

Some kidney patients reducing phosphorus in their diet might need to avoid boxed macaroni and cheese mix. This soft, high protein and nutrient-dense version is easy to prepare from scratch and only one pot! The major trick to this pasta is the use of fall fat sour cream, you can substitute an equal amount of plain Greek yogurt and it will up the protein but be grainy and not smooth. To be low fat but still creamy, you will need to substitute a mixture of Neufchatel cheese and Greek yogurt. It is also important to use very sharp cheese and not plain cheddar to get the proper flavor. The nice thing about this meal is that it is one that can be shared by the family. It can be a welcome treat to be able to eat the same food, together at a meal.

- 1 pound macaroni noodles
- 8 oz shredded sharp cheddar cheese
- 1 cup full-fat sour cream (low fat: 4 ounces cubed Neufchatel cheese and one-half cup Greek yogurt)
- 2 teaspoons yellow mustard
- Salt and pepper to taste

Boil the pasta according to the package instructions. Turn off heat, drain. After draining, add all the sour cream and the mustard and stir well. Add the shredded cheese one third at a time and stir well after each addition. Add salt and pepper (if allowed) to taste and serve.

MINI MEATLOAVES

Because feeding someone who is convalescing can be a challenge, it is helpful to batch cook. These small meatloaves bake in a muffin pan so they are already pre-portioned (making it easy to freeze some for later). Use lean ground beef to avoid large amounts of liquid fat in the muffin tin. If you need these to be gluten-free, blend 1 ½ cups of rolled oats in the blender to make fine flour and use instead of the regular flour in this recipe.

- 1 ½ pounds lean ground beef
- 2 whole eggs, beaten
- 1 cup bread crumbs (or 1 ½ cups rolled oats pulverized in a blender)
- 1 carrot, peeled and grated
- ½ cup heavy whipping cream
- ½ teaspoon dried parsley
- ½ teaspoon rubbed sage
- Salt and pepper to taste

Grease the cups of a twelve-cup muffin tin and preheat the oven to 350F. Whisk together the cream and the eggs and stir in the bread crumbs or oatmeal flour. Let stand five to eight minutes to allow the flour to absorb the liquid before stirring in the shredded carrot. Combine the remaining ingredients with the liquid ingredients and mix until thoroughly blended. Evenly portion into the twelve cups of the muffin tin and press into even layers within the tray. Bake for 25 minutes or until internal temperature reaches 160F or juices run clear. Remove from tin and cool before wrapping in foil and freezing. To reheat, bake in a preheated in 350F for 20-25 minutes until thoroughly warm.

CHICKEN SALAD SPREAD

- 3TB olive oil
- 2lb boneless chicken thighs (about three), cubed
- 3 medium apples, peeled and chopped
- 3 medium carrots, peeled and chopped
- 1 cup white wine (or substitute with one tablespoon apple cider vinegar plus enough water or broth to equal a cup)
- 2 cup broth
- 2 tsp dried parsley
- 1 tsp dried marjoram
- ½-1 tsp black pepper (if allowed)
- Salt or salt substitute to taste
- 1 cup sour cream
- 1 cup plain Greek yogurt (full fat preferred)

In a large skillet, brown chicken pieces with apples and carrots. Once the carrots begin to weep or lose liquid into the pot, add the wine (or the vinegar substitute) as well as the herbs, pepper, and salt. Bring to a boil and turn down to a simmer. Cook for 15 minutes. Drain and place in a food processor and blend until finely chopped. Add sour cream and Greek yogurt and blend until smooth. This can be eaten hot or refrigerated and used cold as a sandwich spread.

WATCHED POT HARD BOILED EGGS

Boiled eggs are high in protein in and good fats and mash easily making them a good addition to many diets. Preparing a dozen at a time and keeping them in the fridge gives a busy caregiver lots of options for fast meals and snacks. It is also easy to ask friends and family to make these when they want to help but you aren't confident in their ability to manage the needs of a complex diet. This technique gives you perfectly boiled eggs with creamy yolks that are not green or dry or crumbly. Use a pot large enough to keep the eggs in a single layer in the bottom with just a little bit of wiggle room.

- Eggs
- Water

Cover the bottom of your pot with as many eggs as you can (or want!) but do keep them in a single layer. Cover the eggs completely with cold water and about one inch over. Place pot on the stove and set the heat as high as it will go. You will need to watch the pot. As soon as you get a full boil, big bubbles at the surface, cover the pot and move to a cool burner. Set a timer for ten minutes for slightly more creamy eggs (good for adding to aspic or for mashing) and twelve minutes for firm eggs with slices that won't crumble. The firmer eggs are good for adding on top of crackers and for those transitioning to a firmer diet. While the eggs rest, prepare a bowl with ice water. Once the timer has gone off, use a slotted spoon to transfer the eggs to the ice bath. Chill for at least fifteen minutes to thoroughly cool the eggs before using or transfer to the fridge for later use.

EASY OVEN BAKED HARD-COOKED EGGS

Some people just don't have the time to watch the stove and these eggs cook with no attention. I have used this method for well over a decade and only once did I have an egg break. It wasn't even hard to clean up because it cracked into the muffin tray and my oven was still clean. I once used this method to bake two gross of eggs, that is two dozen-dozen eggs, for a catering job where deviled eggs were on the menu. It is brilliantly easy.

- 1 dozen eggs
- 1 twelve cup muffin tray

Set one egg in the bottom of each cup. Preheat your oven to 350F. Once the oven is at temperature, place the eggs in the tray in the oven. Set a timer for 25 minutes. While they bake, prepare an ice water bath. Once the timer has gone off, use a slotted spoon to transfer the eggs to the ice bath, remember that the tray and eggs will both be hot. Chill for at least fifteen minutes to thoroughly cool the eggs before using or transfer to the fridge for later use.

EGG SALAD

Egg salad is a common lunchbox item but don't discredit its nutritional value just because it seems ordinary. Eggs are high in protein and healthy fats as well as a host of vitamins and minerals. They are soft and low residue and make a great addition for lots of diets. Instead of mayo, this recipe relies on the creaminess of nutrient dense sour cream and the added protein of Greek yogurt. This version also does not include chunky ingredients that can be a problem and no high acid ingredients. Instead of mustard, this recipe gets its tang from yogurt and uses turmeric for color and flavor. If you need a low-fat version for your loved one, follow the instructions to increase the Greek yogurt.

- 8 hard-boiled eggs, peeled
- ¼ cup sour cream (omit for low-fat version)
- ¼ cup plain Greek yogurt (for low fat, increase this to ½ cup)
- ½ teaspoon ground turmeric
- Salt and pepper to taste, if allowed

In a medium bowl, mash the eggs with a potato masher until they are proper consistency. Add the yogurt, the sour cream (if using), and the turmeric. Stir well with a fork until well combined. Adjust the seasoning with salt and pepper. Serve cold and refrigerate leftovers.

CHAPTER EIGHT: FRUITS AND DESSERTS

"But the fruit of the Spirit is love, joy, peace, longsuffering, gentleness, goodness, faith, gentleness, self-control..." Galatians 5:23

DESSERTS STILL HAVE THEIR PLACE in convalescent diets. A treat can really boost the mood of your loved ones when they have a lot of emotional work they are doing while they are healing. These are also good recipes to turn to when you have more resistant eaters. Children are infamously challenging when they are sick and often refuse to eat or self-limit to treat foods. These desserts are not completely without nutritional value and most of them have additional protein and are nutrient-dense which means that you can feel better about serving them. Because protein is very important in restoring lost muscle following a severe illness, I have prioritized it in these recipes.

You don't have to be limited to serving complex foods. Don't forget that Greek yogurt, plain or flavored, and cottage cheese are delicious drizzled with a little honey and allowed fruit. Both are very high in protein and are great staples to keep on hand and while they can feel like a treat, they are definitely a healthy meal. Many diets will require only cooked fruits but if this is too much for you right now, turn to things like jarred applesauce and even baby food fruits. Having these on hand can ensure a quick and healthy snack even when time and strength are short. If you are looking for more treat recipes, there are also some good ones in the Gelatin section to try.

BERRY COMPOTE

This is a quick and easy sauce that can be made in less than ten minutes. It is delicious when served on cooked cereals or over yogurt and cottage cheese or ice cream. It will easily puree in a food processor or with a stick blender.

- 16 ounces berries such as strawberries, blueberries, raspberries, blackberries
- 2 Tablespoons juice such as lemon, lime, orange, or apple
- ½ teaspoon vanilla or almond extract
- 2 Tablespoons honey (can be omitted)

Add all ingredients in a small pot and heat over medium. After about five minutes, begin to stir and mash with a potato masher for another five minutes until the berries are soft and steamy. Honey will make the sauce slightly thicker and sweeter but it is not absolutely necessary. This will keep for five days or so in the fridge but it can also be frozen for later use. It is lovely warmed slightly in the microwave but it is also good straight from the fridge.

HIGH PROTEIN MILKSHAKE

Milkshakes are often recommended for patients on mechanical soft diets but these are usually low in protein and high in sugar and not a great source of nutrition for recovering from illness or injury. This milkshake is higher in protein but still tastes creamy and indulgent. Remember that some patients will need to eat this with a spoon because straws are not always appropriate.

- 2 cups full-fat plain vanilla ice cream, not ice milk, low sugar preferred
- 3/4 cup full-fat cottage cheese
- 1 teaspoon extract such as vanilla, almond, rum, peppermint
- Optional: caramel, chocolate, or strawberry ice cream topping

Blend the ice cream, cottage cheese, and extract in a blender until smooth. Serve by drizzling the sides of the glass with ice cream topping before filling with the milkshake. Drizzle a slight amount on top. You can also just use an opaque glass and drizzle only a small amount of syrup on top. It usually only takes a small amount to convince your loved one to try this dessert.

HIGH PROTEIN SORBET

Ice cream is often recommended for those on a mechanically soft diet but it is low in protein and high in sugar. This frozen fruit purée makes a delicious soft frozen dessert that is satisfyingly sweet but high in protein and nutrient-dense. If your loved one is on a low acid diet, avoid using pineapple or strawberry as both are high in acid. Strawberry should also be avoided for recent mouth or throat surgeries because its red color can mask blood and its seeds can cause problems for those with intestinal concerns. For those on GI soft or low residue diets, bananas and peaches are preferred. This does take a little time to prepare unless you are using bananas which can be processed immediately.

- 2 cups frozen fruit (sliced banana, peaches, mango, pineapple, or strawberry)
- 1 ½ cups full fat (4%) cottage cheese
- 2-4 tablespoons honey (can be omitted)
- Pinch of salt (also can be omitted)
- ½ teaspoon vanilla extract

Thaw the fruit on the counter for one hour. Sliced frozen banana pieces can be used directly from the freezer. Using a food processor, blend until light and fluffy. This does not keep very well so it is best to serve and eat immediately. The cottage cheese makes this a very high protein food but because it is sweet, it is a great option for reluctant eaters or children who are just tired of being sick.

WHIPPED CREAM

This recipe is quick and easy and avoids preservatives which can be problematic for kidney patients especially. While this version will not stay fluffy as long as the commercial non-dairy variety, the powdered sugar helps prevent it from deflating for several hours. In a low sugar diet, this can be replaced with an equal parts blend of an appropriate sweetener and cornstarch. If it begins to separate after an hour or so, it can be fluffed with a fork or whisk. If you need this for a holiday meal, it is nice to know that it can be made several hours ahead of time.

- 1 cup heavy whipping cream
- ½ teaspoon vanilla extract
- 1 Tablespoon powdered sugar OR 2 teaspoons diabetic sweetener blended with 2 teaspoons cornstarch

Combine all ingredients using either a hand mixer, stand mixer, food processor, or stick blender. Depending on the power of your appliance, this might take anywhere from 2-3 minutes to as many as 7-8. Once the mixture is thick enough to hold to the bottom of a spoon pressed on the surface and lifted up, it is ready. If you whip much longer, you will make butter.

WHIPPED COCONUT CREAM

If dairy is limited in the diet, this can make an excellent substitute. The important thing to note is that you must use full-fat coconut milk, not a coconut milk drink. This can be found in cans or aseptic cardboard containers, often in the Asian section. Refrigerate it at least overnight to make sure it is as cold as possible to make it easier to whip. If you are using a can, turn it upside down before refrigerating to make it easier to open on the top. Open the can and pour off the liquid and use only the thick cream which will be at the bottom of the can. Aseptic containers can be more difficult and you might have to cut the box open. Also, note that the boxed kind contains twice as much as a can so you can either double the recipe or divide the cream in half.

- 1 can full-fat coconut milk, only the cream (save the coconut water for another purpose) OR ½ the cream of an aseptic carton of full-fat coconut milk
- 1 teaspoon vanilla extract

- 2 Tablespoons powdered sugar OR 1 Tablespoon diabetic sweetener, and 1 Tablespoon cornstarch

If the kitchen is warm, chill the bowl and beaters in the freezer for 20 minutes or so. Coconut cream is fragile and breaks easily, even with the addition of powdered sugar or cornstarch. Beat ingredients together using a stand or hand mixer or even a stick blender until it resembles soft cream. It will not thicken as much as dairy cream but can be very satisfying for those on dairy-restricted diets who need to avoid the preservatives in the purchased non-dairy toppings.

COCONUT MILK FRUIT SORBET

Sometimes, patients are told to refrain from eating dairy products for a certain period of time. This is often true for throat and mouth injuries and procedures and can cause a certain amount of feeding anxiety since most people recommend ice cream. When no dairy is recommended, this easy-to-prepare frozen fruit sorbet is soothing and cool. If your loved one has any potential for bleeding, say after dental surgery or a tonsillectomy, avoid red fruits. If your loved one is on a low residue diet, choose peaches which are usually allowed. As for the coconut milk, choose full fat and not the variety intended for drinking. That kind is diluted with water and this means it is thinner and less nutrient-dense. When the diet is very limited, it is important to make every bite count!

- 3 cups frozen fruit such as mixed berries, strawberries, peaches
- 1 banana, fresh
- ¾ cup full-fat coconut milk
- 1-4 tablespoons of honey

Combine all ingredients in a blender and process until smooth. You will need to stop and tamp down the ingredients a couple of times. This will actually freeze well in a bread loaf pan and can be later scooped out and served in small portions. This is a good make-ahead recipe to keep in the freezer for when you need it.

FRUIT JUICE GRANITA (CHIPPED ICE)

This is a recipe to keep on hand even when you are not carrying for a recovering loved one. When summer comes around and children are begging for money for the overpriced and none too healthy treats from the ice cream vendor, you can help them make their own special creations at home.

- 32 ounces of allowed fruit juice, no added sugar

- 1 cup granulated sugar
- 1 cup water
- 3-4 pencil-sized sprigs fresh herbs such as basil, mint (optional)
- 2 loaf pans, 9x5

The first step to the process is to make a simple syrup. Not only does this give an energy boost to the final product but it also prevents it from freezing completely, it makes the final result a bit softer and not so hard. Because you are adding syrup, start with a juice that has no added sugar. Add the water, sugar, and herbs (if using) to a saucepan and set on medium-high heat. Stirring occasionally, heat the mixture until the sugar is completely dissolved, or about 1-2 minutes. If using herbs, cover and let rest for 30 minutes, then strain and discard them before continuing. Stir in the juice and combine completely before dividing between the two loaf pans. Freeze for one hour and then scrape the mixture with a fork to break it up. Return to the freezer for half an hour and then scrape once again. You will need to repeat this process over and over for about three hours but once it resembles sand and no liquid remains, it is ready. It is something like a snow cone and can be served in small dishes. You can also use this base in popsicle molds without having to scrape.

CHAPTER NINE: VEGETABLES

"Better is a dinner of herbs where love is than a fatted calf with hatred." Proverbs 15:17

MANY OF THE VEGETABLES YOU WILL NEED to serve a convalescent will be pureed to make them soft to eat and readily digestible. There are two types of vegetables that work well as purees and they fall into two categories: starchy and high water. These foods are prepared as purees in the same basic way but have two different bases. The high-water foods need the addition of starch to make them thicker, often white or sweet potato is added to create the proper balance. Both kinds begin with the food cut into pieces of the same size so that they cook evenly and finish at the same time, the exception is the rice which is prepared as normal. Boil the foods until they are soft enough to be mashed between two spoons. The smaller the pieces, the faster they will cook, and always cook in water that is twice as much in volume as the vegetables being cooked.

Starchy Fruits, Vegetables and Grains	High Water Vegetables

Potatoes	Carrots
Lentils*	Turnip*
Beans*	Celeriac*
Peas*	Cauliflower*
Rice	Asparagus*
Apples	Celery*
Sweet Potato	Green Beans
Pie pumpkin	
*These foods are not appropriate for low-residue diets	

You might have seen baby food in the store with labels that say things like "strained peas" or "strained carrots" and they don't mean boiled and drained. In this case, it means that the food has been mashed and pressed through a screen or fine strainer to get out any fibrous bits. This makes for a creamy smooth puree that is safer for babies and convalescents to eat. If you are trying to make a smooth puree but not necessarily trying to serve a low-residue diet, fibrous foods can be pressed through a sieve using a spoon after being blended in a food processor or by using a stick blender. The screens of these mills can be hard to clean so dedicate a stiff bristled toothbrush for scrubbing these items and wash them immediately after use. Because the washing up is a challenge, making larger amounts allows you to only have to clean once. Once the food is cooked, drained, blended, and perhaps run through a strainer or food mill, then the base is ready for the addition of the fat.

Vegetable Puree Base	
Starchy Foods	High Water Foods
<ul><li>Chopped, boiled, drained food of choice.</li><li>Food might be "strained".</li><li>Addition of cream, butter, or milk equal to 1/3 of the weight of the food being pureed.</li></ul>	<ul><li>Chopped food of choice.</li><li>Addition of chopped starchy food, such as white or sweet potato, equal to about 25% of the weight of the primary food.</li><li>Food is boiled, drained, and might be strained.</li><li>Addition of butter, cream, milk, or the cream of a can</li></ul>

	of coconut milk equal to ⅓ weight of the food being pureed.

Starchy foods need an addition of ⅓ of their weight (the weight before cooking) of a fat such as cream, butter, milk, or a combination of any of these to create a truly creamy puree. The final result is not only more nutrient-dense but the fat allows for the better absorption of some vitamins that are fat soluble. If avoiding dairy, use full-fat coconut milk or a small bit of oil along with another milk substitute. High water foods need to be prepared with a portion of the base containing starchy food, like potatoes, before continuing with the addition of dairy or substitute. The starch works to thicken the puree and help hold the liquid into the puree. Without it, the puree will be grainy and will "weep" or the liquid will puddle under the food. An example of how to use this basic formula to make purees is below.

HOMEMADE PUREED VEGETABLES

SWEET POTATO PUREE
(STARCHY FOOD EXAMPLE)

- 3-4 large sweet potatoes (~1.5 lbs.),
- Water
- Salt (if allowed in diet)
- Half a stick of butter (4 Tablespoons)
- ¼ Cup heavy cream
- Dairy-free option: Instead of butter and cream, add 4 Tablespoons of olive oil and ¼ cup non-dairy milk substitute

Peel and chop 3-4 large sweet potatoes in small dice. Place in a large pot, and cover with water to about twice the depth of sweet potatoes. You can add 1-2 teaspoons of salt to the water, if allowed. Bring to a boil and turn down to a simmer. Cook until the pieces can be mashed between two spoons. Cooking time will depend on the size of the pieces. Drain the food before processing.

Process in a food processor or with a stick blender. Sweet potatoes don't need to be strained, but more fibrous foods might need to be. Using the food processor or stick blender, add half a stick of butter (4 Tablespoons) and ¼ cup of heavy cream (or dairy-free substitutes) and process until smooth.

CARROT PUREE
(HIGH WATER FOOD EXAMPLE)

- 6 large carrots (~1 lb.)
- 1 small potato, or half of a large potato (~¼ lb.)

- Water
- Salt if allowed
- Half a stick of butter (4 Tablespoons)
- ¼ Cup heavy cream
- Dairy-free option: Instead of butter and cream, add 4 Tablespoons of olive oil and ¼ cup non-dairy milk substitute

Peel and chop 6 large carrots into thin coins. These should weigh about one pound total. Peel and chop one small or half of a large potato into similar size pieces. This should weigh about ¼ pound. Place both the carrots and potatoes in a large pot, and cover with water to about two times the depth of the food. You can add 1-2 of salt to the water, if allowed. Bring to a boil, and then turn heat down to a simmer. Cook until the pieces can be mashed between two spoons. Cooking time will depend on the thickness of the slices.

Drain the food before processing. Process in a food processor or with a stick blender. Carrots don't need to be strained, but more fibrous foods might need to be. Using the food processor or stick blender, add half a stick (4 Tablespoons butter) and ¼ cup of heavy cream (or dairy-free substitutes) and process until smooth.

FIRMING PUREES FOR MOLDING

To firm these purees for molding, use ⅛ teaspoon xanthan gum per cup of mashed food. Using a blender, add the xanthan gum all at once, and blend until thickened. The puree will now be firm even if reheated. When molding food, be sure to cover tightly over the top with plastic wrap or freezer paper or the silicon lid that comes with medical molds. Press it down and wipe the palm of the hand over the surface to keep it smooth and press out all air bubbles. **It is critical that the food sets up with no "skin" or dried surface that could be difficult for your loved one to eat.** Cool the food thoroughly before freezing. Remove from the silicon mold, and freeze in an appropriate container. You can easily take out a couple of molded pieces and thaw on a plate and warm in a microwave before serving.

MAPLE CINNAMON CARROTS

Carrots have a natural sweetness and are allowed on most diets. This dish adds maple and cinnamon, which add an almost desert-like flavor, which makes them a great addition to meals served to picky or reluctant eaters. These are very soft as they are prepared, but they can be either mashed to processed with a stick blender to make a quick puree. This makes a nice dish to serve the whole family, and it is easy enough to puree just a portion. **If cooking for a someone with acid reflux or on a low residue diet, swap out the cinnamon for cardamom. This spice, common in Scandinavian cooking, won't aggravate heartburn.**

- 5 large carrots, peeled and sliced into coins (this is about a pound)
- 4 Tablespoons butter, diced
- 2 Tablespoon maple syrup
- 2 teaspoons cinnamon (optional: substitute cardamom)

Add the carrots and butter to a large sauce pan, and cook over medium high heat, stirring occasionally. Cook until the carrots are soft enough to mash with a spoon, usually 16-18 minutes. Stir in the maple syrup and cinnamon (or cardamom), if using. For pureed diets, you can mash with a potato masher, adding water until it is the proper texture, or use a stick blender.

BUTTERED SPICED BEETS

Beets are appropriate for a wide variety of diets, and they provide a beautiful pop of color to the dinner plate. You can mash a portion of this recipe to provide an even softer food for your loved one to eat, while the remainder can be served as is for the rest of the family. Being able to eat similarly with the family is a morale booster for a convalescent.

- 5 medium beets, peeled and finely diced (About a pound)
- 4 Tablespoons butter, diced

- 1 teaspoon cinnamon
- 1 teaspoon crystallized ginger
- ¼ cup water
- Salt and pepper, if allowed

Melt the butter in a larger pot, and add the diced beets, cinnamon, ginger, and water. Cover and cook over medium for 15 minutes. Remove lid, and stir well. Continue to cook, uncovered, stirring occasionally until the beets are soft and most of the water is evaporated. Season with salt and pepper, if using, and serve.

CREAMED SPINACH

Spinach is full of vitamins and minerals, and adding cream and parmesan is a great way to get picky eaters to try a bite. This version is a quick, stove top version that you can finish while taking care of other kitchen chores. Look for bags of either baby spinach or chopped spinach to make the dish faster to throw together. If the spinach pieces are too large, it can be hard for patients to eat.

- 2 pounds baby spinach or chopped
- 3 Tablespoons butter
- 16 ounces sour cream (substitute fat-free Greek yogurt for low fat)
- ½ Cup grated parmesan

- Black pepper to taste, as allowed

In a large skillet, melt the butter and add the spinach. Cook over medium heat, stirring occasionally. Cook until thoroughly wilted and the liquid begins to weep out. This will take 6-8 minutes. Stir in the sour cream and parmesan and season with pepper, if using.

OVEN ROASTED ZUCCHINI

Zucchini has a mellow, earthy flavor with a sweetness that is intensified by roasting. Too often, oven baked dishes are cooked at too low of a temperature and it means that the zucchini steams in its own moisture which dulls the flavor and texture. This version is cooked at a high temperature, and it yields a soft flesh and brighter flavor. For low residue, GI soft, and puree diets you will need to remove the skin before cooking.

- 3 medium zucchinis split in half lengthwise and again crosswise
- 3-4 Tablespoons olive oil
- ¼ Cup parmesan
- Black pepper to taste, if using

Preheat the oven to 450F. Place the zucchini halves on a sheet pan and cover with the olive oil and toss liberally. Spread across the pan with lots of room to allow the steam to evaporate without cooking the pieces next to each other. Roast for 10-20 minutes, the time depends on the size of your pieces. Start checking at 10 minutes and then every two minutes until the pieces are soft and starting to brown nicely. Remove from oven and sprinkle liberally with the parmesan and black pepper, if using.

CONCLUSION

"He saith unto him the third time, Simon, son of Jonas, lovest thou me? Peter was grieved because he said unto him the third time, Lovest thou me? And he said unto him, Lord, thou knowest all things; thou knowest that I love thee. Jesus saith unto him, Feed my sheep." John 21:17

ONE OF THE SINCERE PRIVILEGES of my life is to have known the great but uncanonized saint, Ann Sullivan of Aurora, Colorado. She lived in an eastern suburb of Denver, blocks away from the city line. She was a deeply pious Catholic woman, a daily communicant, a fixture of my childhood, and now a permanent monument to hospitality in my adulthood. More than any other person I have ever known, Mrs. Sullivan knew how to care for others and how to make each and every person she ever met feel as if they were deeply loved. She mattered for many reasons, but one of the most significant is because she made others feel that they mattered.

Ann Sullivan prayed constantly, and as a devout Catholic, she always had a rosary with her. She used it to pray for everyone she knew, random people she saw in public, those she came across in her work, famous people living scandalous lives, and scores of needy folks whose names were slipped to her by others who wanted someone a little closer to Jesus to pray with them. She loved people not just with prayer but with food. Her kitchen was warm and cluttered and the epitome of home comfort, and there she cooked delicious food for others. She was regionally famous, especially for her chocolate cake and her fried chicken. It still happens, more than a decade later, that mentioning her name conjures up memories of meals she cooked for others, ones that fed heart and soul and not just bellies.

I grew up in Denver, where I went to school with her youngest child. Ann Sullivan had a policy of having whole groups of her children's friends come to the house for dinner and to pray the rosary before going out. Her kids were popular and always well-liked, and this means that there were lots of teenagers at her house. Her policy was solid. When out for the night and deciding what movie to see or if a party was worth going to, kids couldn't help but feel the carryover of the rosary and dinner at her house. It made the right decisions easier to make.

As an adult, my husband and I tired of living in the urban center and bought a house in her neighborhood. We lived directly next door to one of her children and up the street from another and down the street from a third. When I was pregnant with my ninth child, the one born before my train wreck birth, Mrs. Sullivan was diagnosed with advanced and aggressive colon cancer. It was terminal, but she chose chemo in order to lengthen her life by a few months. She did it because one of her nine kids had just carried her children through the sudden death on Christmas Eve of their other grandmother. She wanted to not ruin another Christmas for her grandchildren, and by sheer force of will, muscled through to Easter. I was on the regular roster of people bringing her household meals as she coped with the effects of intensive chemotherapy that could not save her but only delay her death.

I remember the last meal that I made for her and her husband and their adult developmentally delayed daughter; it was enchiladas made with homemade tortillas and scratch-made sauce. I made it because I knew that her daughter loved these, and I thought it would be a fun last treat before I delivered my baby by cesarean section the next day, which would leave me off the meal rotation for a bit. I would have to have my gallbladder removed immediately after delivering my daughter, and it is that incision that herniated and was the first falling domino in my crisis two years later. I brought dinner over in my red ceramic casserole dish, one I still use thirteen years later.

The next day, my gallbladder removal was complicated. I had an attack during my surgery and I passed stones into my liver ducts. As soon as I woke up, the nurses told me that I was not permitted liquids, because I would need another procedure–one that didn't involve incisions because they could go through the mouth–but was necessary to clear the ducts. It would mean a longer hospital stay, and I was crushed. I just wanted to be home with my children and new baby, and I admit to crying until my belly incisions hurt. But this isn't about me. This is about Mrs. Sullivan.

Looking at her last days, home and resting with her family as cancer took its toll, Ann Sullivan was moved by concern for my family. She got out of her bed and went to her kitchen and baked my children one of her famous scratch chocolate cakes with creamy chocolate frosting, and she baked it in my dish. Her husband brought the dish to my house with her regards and told the children that she knew that they missed me and that she hoped the chocolate would help. She never returned a dish empty until her cancer became overwhelming, and that day she went back to her ingrained habit even though she was dying. It is funny how a single dessert can last so many years, long after the food is eaten and the dish is washed and dried and put away. I say a little prayer for her every time I use it, every time I see it in the cupboard, every time I serve food in it. It was the last food that she was able to prepare for anyone, because she died just ten days later. She rose from her bed of pain to feed my children. I did not see her again after I dropped off her supper until I saw her in her coffin at her funeral.

People fussed over me at the funeral, bringing me a footrest and trying to keep me comfortable at the services. I insisted on going, but I was uncomfortable with the attention. This was never about me; this was about her. I needed to say goodbye to one of the greatest women I will ever know, but more importantly, I needed to pray for the woman who prayed for every other person she ever met. Mrs. Sullivan was a nurse. She spent her days lovingly caring for people who were sick, hurt, and frightened, and she spent her nights praying for them. She spread love everywhere she went. It dripped from her rosary and radiated out from her hands in the food that she prayerfully cooked and served others. Her funeral was full to bursting with hundreds of bereft mourners who had been supported by her, fed by her, buoyed by her advice, and whom she had held in her arms.

She had this incredible ability to reach out and make each and every single person she met know that they were important, that they meant something to her, that they were someone who mattered to her. Her love cut through loneliness and isolation like a knife, and she let the light shine in. The void she left behind was unsettling; it was like looking up at the sky and not seeing the sun. Despite the fact that she was no longer on earth, her love continued to shine down on everyone she ever loved.

The night of my own crisis, two years later, Ann Sullivan's daughter woke up in the middle of the night. Erin later told me that she felt a race of panic and could not understand why, but she remembered her mother's advice. Mrs. Sullivan always told her children that when they woke up in the middle of the night, God was calling them to pray for someone, that someone needed them. So, Erin prayed. Despite the fact that she believed my delivery had gone well, she prayed for me. I know with every fiber of my being that Ann Sullivan woke Erin up to pray for me as I was unconscious and bleeding out in an operating theater while my husband panicked all alone, waiting in my hospital room. Five hours later, I was in the intensive care unit and sedated while a ventilator breathed for me. I survived the night not solely by the skill of the surgeons but also by God's benevolent grace and the prayers of others.

Erin is very much her mother's daughter. She did not know what she could do for us, so she fed my family while I lingered in the intensive care unit. She went to her kitchen and made a huge quantity of her mother's famous fried chicken, and she brought it to my family. Cooking for a family with nine children is no mean feat, but having grown up in a large family and having a large family of her own, she was prepared. Besides, she is Ann Sullivan's daughter. This is what Sullivans do; they feed others.

The work that you do when you care for others is exhausting and consuming. It feels thankless and invisible. Even when it feels that it is pointless, it isn't really. When it feels like there are other things that you could or should be doing, know that this work is critical and valuable. When we care for others, we become the innkeeper caring for the man rescued by the Good Samaritan, and we become Simon who feeds Jesus' sheep. This is holy work, and it is hard, and it can leave you feeling spent. But it is no less good. No matter what else we could be doing, we are doing what Christ Himself asks us to do. We are feeding His sheep.

You will need rest for yourself. You will need respite. When you step away from this work to breathe for yourself for a bit, remember what it is that you do. Fill up on love so that you can turn around and love others, working out your salvation in still and quiet moments marked by acts of love and compassion. Loving people is quiet. Ann Sullivan was not flashy or loud, and outside of Denver, most people will never have heard of her, but this does not mean she was not profoundly important or that her quiet life did not speak volumes. Her love continues to radiate, long after she has gone to her reward. Her meals live on and continue to feed everyone who came in contact with her during her too-brief life. Mrs. Sullivan is a mentor, a model, for all of us to follow. From her, we can learn to love hard and how to care for others in life-changing and transformative ways. May she pray for us always that we become closer to the person that she was on Earth. She was far holier than I ever will be and will sit closer to Jesus than I will but maybe she will let me come sit with her sometimes. May Ann Sullivan keep you company on your journey in hospitality and may she open the door to the inn when you come to it. Until then, may God keep you and bless you and make you a saint.

"May the road rise up to meet you. May the wind be always at your back. May the sun shine warm upon your face; the rains fall soft upon your fields and until we meet again, may God hold you in the palm of His hand." -Irish Proverb

MRS. SULLIVAN'S FRIED CHICKEN

- 6 leg quarters, split into thighs and drumsticks
- 3 Cups buttermilk
  ### BREADING:
- 2 1/2 Cups all-purpose flour
- 1 Cup corn starch
- 1 Tablespoon salt
- 1 Tablespoon paprika
- 1 Tablespoon granulated garlic (not salt)
- 1-2 teaspoon pepper
- Optional: 1-2 tsp red pepper flakes
- At least 1 Quart fryer oil. (I recommend peanut because of its high smoke point.)

Marinate the chicken in buttermilk for at least four hours, or overnight. Drain and discard liquid. Thoroughly dredge chicken in the breading mixture.

In a heavy Dutch oven, heat at least 3/4-1 inch of oil to 350F. You will need to fry in batches and allow oil to rebound back to the proper temperature between batches. Oil that is too cool will make your chicken greasy. Oil that is too hot will cook the outside but leave the interior undercooked, which is unsafe. Chicken should be cooked to 160F and allowed to rise to 165F before serving. It will gain a few degrees because of residual heat. Add chicken with plenty of space between pieces. Cook for seven minutes per side, turning once.

To hold chicken until all batches are cooked, set a rack over a cookie sheet with low sides. Place cooked pieces on this rack, and keep in a preheated 170F oven while you cook subsequent batches. Then you can serve all the chicken at once.

MRS. SULLIVAN'S CHOCOLATE CAKE

- ¾ Cup Dutch cocoa
- 2 Cups sugar, plus additional for pan
- 1 ¾ Cup All Purpose flour
- 2 teaspoon baking powder
- 1 teaspoon baking soda

- 1 teaspoon salt
- 2 eggs
- 1 Cup milk
- 1 stick butter (8 Tablespoons), melted and cooled slightly (plus additional for greasing pan)
- 2 teaspoon vanilla
- 1 Cup boiling water or hot black coffee

Preheat oven to 350F. Grease a 9x13 cake pan with butter, and use sugar to coat well to allow cake to release easily. (This is a trick I learned from my husband's grandmother.) Sift together baking powder, baking soda, and salt. In a separate bowl, whisk cocoa and boiling water or coffee, if using. Once combined, whisk in butter. Then add in milk and vanilla. Add eggs one at a time, whisking well after each addition. Add dry ingredients all at once and whisk only until just combined. Add batter to pan, and smooth well. Bake for 35-40 minutes until toothpick pulls out with only a few crumbs. Cool before frosting.

FROSTING:
- 2 Cups dark chocolate chips
- 1 ¼ Cups heavy whipping cream
- ¼ teaspoon salt
- 1 Tablespoon vanilla extract

Add chocolate to a medium sized metal bowl. Bring cream just to a boil and pour over chocolate and let stand five minutes without touching. After five minutes, beat well with a wooden spoon. Once combined, add salt and vanilla and stir well. Cool in refrigerator for two hours before beating with either a stand mixer and hand mixer. Once light and fluffy, use to frost cake.

ABOUT THE AUTHOR

Melissa Naasko's gift of setting people at ease with her warm competence and kindness shines in this collection of recipes and kitchen skills that support loved ones as they recuperate. Pull up a chair and learn from her experience as a granddaughter of healing family cooks, a mother of eleven, a caterer, and a priest's wife (matushka) in the rugged wilderness of the Upper Peninsula of Michigan where her husband serves a church attached to a monastery. Melissa enjoys writing and speaking to mothers' groups and homeschooling conferences on topics of faith, food, and family.

ABOUT PARK END BOOKS

Park End Books is a traditional publisher bringing beautiful, accessible Orthodox and Catholic books to market. Read more at ParkEndBooks.com

New From Park End Books:

Into the Flames
& Other Plays on Saints' Lives
By Christine Siampos

Enter the story of six saints' lives with these dynamic, performance-proven plays for youth ages 8 and up. These plays make perfect Vacation Church School projects or additions to your youth program. They're presented in order of the feast days of the Saints, from April to December for ease of planning. Learn immersively about St. Innocent of Alaska, Holy Queen Tamar, St. Paraskevi, St. Panteleimon, St. Nicholas of Myra, and the Three Holy Youths, and bring your church family into the story in a way that they will remember!

The Grace of Being There:
Single Mother Saints in Our Lives

Eight Orthodox and Catholic women who have lived single parent life bring you the fruits of their connection with eight women saints who were single mothers in this encouraging collection of essays. Learn about the Widow of Zarephath, St. Photini, St. Helen, St. Anthousa, St. Monica, St. Sophia, St. Margaret of Cortona, and St. Maria of Paris as their lives intertwine with the lived experiences of faithful women who pray to them for help. Discover the grace of being there from women whose lives show you the God who meets every mother right where she is.